Sunshine and Shadow
Depression and Spirituality

Bertha Catherine Madott

Sunshine and Shadow
Depression and Spirituality

NOVALIS

Sunshine and Shadow: Depression and Spirituality is published by Novalis © 1996

Cover and illustrations: Anna Payne-Krzyzanowski

Layout: Christiane Lemire, Francine Petitclerc

Novalis Business Offices, 49 Front St. East, Second Floor, Toronto, Ontario, M5E 1B3

Novalis Editorial Offices, 223 Main St., Ottawa, Ontario, K1S 1C4

Printed in Canada.

Canadian Cataloguing in Publication Data

Madott, Bertha Catherine, 1948-
  Sunshine and shadow: depression and spirituality

Includes bibliographical references and index.
ISBN 2-89088-828-2

  1. Depression, Mental—Religious aspects—
Christianity.   I. Title.

BV4910.34.M33   1996   248.8'6   C96-900706-X

Dedication

No book is ever created in a vacuum, especially a book as personal as this one. I am grateful to Dr. Stanley Debow for his wisdom and patience: this book would never have been written without him. Likewise, my family has been unfailingly supportive, bringing sunshine and encouragement into my life day after day.
I treasure the honesty and courage of the friends who shared their personal struggles with me; without their insights, my understanding of the shadows of life would be far more limited. In the same way, those who attend my retreats and workshops on prayer, hope and various aspects of spirituality have taught me countless lessons of courage and faith. Dr. Peter Moran, Department of Psychiatry, Mount Sinai Hospital, reviewed Part I of the manuscript and gave me important and timely medical advice.

To everyone who touched my life during this writing, my sincerest thanks.

NOVALIS

Contents

Part III: Hiding under the Shadow

Part IV: Into the Sunshine

Part I

Crying in the Darkness

. . . the meaning and treatment of depression . . .

1. Crying in the Darkness: Definitions of Depression

Many deeply creative and spiritual people have battled depression, a silent but potentially devastating disease. These are the powerful words and images they use to describe their experiences:

. . . black dogs encircling me . . .

. . . like someone turned off the light . . .

. . . going from *Technicolor* to *black and white* . . .

. . . climbing out of a pit, dust and ashes everywhere . . . .

As we begin our exploration of the sunshine and shadow of this illness, let's look more closely at the descriptions and definitions used by professionals when talking about depression.

Everyone feels blue sometimes; even the most cheerful among us has days when nothing seems to go right. We grieve when a friend or relative dies; we cry when we hear bad news; we feel dazed and confused if we lose a job. These are normal human reactions, appropriate responses to the heartaches and headaches of life. This is not depression.

On the other hand, *clinical depression* is a term used by professionals to distinguish a condition that is longer and more severe than normal reactions to stress, grief and loss. A parent dies, and we are still swamped with sadness more than a year later; we cry for no apparent reason, even when things are going well; we have a career that used to be satisfying, but now we are unable to concentrate or enjoy our work. This is *clinical depression*.

What is this sometimes mysterious and always unpleasant disease that affects so many of us? The Canadian Mental Health Association gives this simple answer: "Depression is an illness affecting mind and body. At times, almost everyone feels *down, blue* or *sad* and becomes discouraged with life, but usually these mood changes are temporary. However, when a depressed mood persists for one or two months, causes a person to feel miserable and sad in many ways and begins to interfere with everyday living, it is likely to be the sign of a serious state of depression that requires outside help."[1]

Those who have never experienced the devastation caused by this illness are often unable to imagine the sadness, frustration and exhaustion that accompany depression. They offer helpful advice meant to cheer up the patient; they can't understand why anyone who has "all this to live for" should be so cranky, tired and dissatisfied! But this is the very point of true *clinical depression*: our moods and emotions, thoughts and behaviour are no longer linked to the normal cause-and-effect mechanisms that used to work reasonably well in our brains. We can't sleep even when we're tired; we eat when we're not hungry; we cry when we have no reason to be sad.

Furthermore, normally enjoyable activities — holidays, gatherings of old friends, delicious meals — give us no pleasure. Many depressed people, contrary to popular belief, work very hard to live a normal life. We try desperately to "pull up our socks," as we are so often advised to do, and are baffled that our efforts are unsuccessful. For a long time we

---

[1]   1993 fact sheet on depression, Canadian Mental Health Association, Ontario division.

fear that something is physically wrong with us, complaining about insomnia, stomach aches, nausea, diarrhoea, headaches, chest pains. Although better education has made the medical profession more aware of depression than in the past, doctors sometimes make the wrong diagnosis. Relying on outdated stereotypes, they have trouble believing that the successful, well-dressed patient whom they have known for years is now trying to cope with a mental illness.

Depression is in fact the most common mental illness; one in four women and one in ten men can expect to develop depression in their lives. It affects young and old, rich and poor, married and single. Thankfully, it is also a disease that responds particularly well to treatment. Eighty percent of those with depression can feel better and recover when they receive appropriate treatment.[2]

No one chooses depression; it is not a failure of the will, a sign of weakness, or the result of bad behaviour. On the contrary: depressed people are often perfectionists with a highly developed sense of responsibility. Dragging oneself out of bed when every day's prospects are dry and dismal takes far more courage than many of life's more dramatic challenges. It is an act of bravery for most depressed people to get up every morning to face another day.

This book will stress the links between depression and spirituality. All of us are composed of body and soul, mind, will and heart, inextricably bound together. We cannot isolate soul from body, and the sufferings and struggles of body and mind are affected by the condition of the spirit, and vice versa. Furthermore, we struggle to make sense of the presence of illness in a world created by a loving God. The desire to find the point of this life's journey is especially strong when the journey is not going well. We need every scrap of comfort and consolation that is available to us when we're depressed, including the resources of prayer and meditation.

Jesus drew upon the wisdom of his ancestors when he quoted from the Book of Deuteronomy, telling his followers that the greatest commandment is to "love the Lord your God with all your heart, and

---

[2]   Ibid.

with all your soul, and with all your mind, and with all your strength."[3] He then instructed his followers to love their neighbours as they love themselves. Many writers on spirituality focus on the multitude of ways in which we can love God and our neighbours; very few deal with the individual as a complete human person equally needing love and compassion. Because self-hatred is such a prominent factor in the experience of depression, this book will focus on learning to love the self, first of all by understanding and treating a disease that makes life seem utterly loveless and futile. Inspired by the Judeo-Christian tradition, this book will invite the reader to love every dimension of the human self — body and soul, mind and strength — so that, while learning to love ourselves, we can also turn our love towards God and those around us.

2. Symptoms of Depression

Let's take a closer look at the symptoms associated with depression, the signs that professionals notice when putting together a diagnosis. No one will experience *all* of these symptoms at once — and thank God for that — but anyone who has been troubled by more than five of these for an extended period of time (more than two weeks) might suspect depression. Note: to make a diagnosis of a "major depressive episode," one of the symptoms must be either depressed mood or sadness, *or* loss of interest or pleasure.

- *Depressed mood or sadness.* It is normal to feel sad during a funeral, but feeling sad for no discernible reason while eating dinner or watching a ball game is a sign that something is wrong. Sadness is often associated with *crying*. People with depression cry frequently for no apparent reason.

- *Loss of interest or pleasure in your usual activities*, including grooming, hobbies, housework and social activities. You have been an avid golfer for twenty years and suddenly you can't be bothered getting your clubs out this spring. Life is boring and pointless; everything is a big waste of time, even taking a bath or washing

---

[3]   Mark 12:28. Jesus is referring to Deuteronomy 6:4. Unless otherwise noted, all biblical quotations are from *The New Oxford Annotated Bible - New Revised Standard Version* (New York: Oxford University Press, 1991).

your clothes. Sex is more trouble than it's worth. Negative phrases like "Who cares?" or "What's the point?" are often in your thoughts. It's easier to be alone than to go out with others. These are important signals that something is out of balance inside.

Other symptoms are:

- *Inability to concentrate.* Thinking suddenly becomes hard work, routine tasks take much longer than usual and normally sharp memory becomes unreliable. Related to this is *difficulty making decisions.* Even the most trivial choices — chocolate versus vanilla ice cream — are hard to make. Confronting more complex and important decisions is a major challenge.

- *Restlessness and agitation.* We can learn something by watching body language. Flitting from one activity to another, fidgeting, nail-biting, hair-pulling — these can be warning signs. Depressed people may use words like *edgy, squirrely*[4] or *jumpy* to describe themselves, because depressed people often suffer from anxiety as well.

- *Insomnia.* Sleep disturbances are especially common. Some sufferers can't fall asleep, some can't stay asleep, some wake up far too early. Everyone has a bad night once in a while, but chronic insomnia (longer than four weeks) is usually a sign of other problems.

- *Too much sleep.* In contrast there are those who find themselves sleeping away their lives — up to twenty hours a day under the covers. This is less common than insomnia.

- *Loss of appetite.* To the depressed person, food often loses all appeal. It is a struggle to eat; everything tastes or smells "funny." Watch for sudden, unwanted weight loss.

---

4   Squirrels can safely eat poisonous mushrooms; they are not harmed by the toxins, but residues of these remain in their tissues. Hunters who then eat the squirrels (Brunswick stew is the name of one traditional dish) thus consume the poisonous mushroom toxins and consequently act strangely or "squirrely." This origin of a popular expression was suggested by the naturalists at Awenda Provincial Park, Penetanguishene, Ontario.

- *Uncontrolled appetite.* At the other extreme are those who are hungry all the time, craving quantities of sweets, fats and comfort foods. This symptom is less common than loss of appetite.

- *Fatigue.* One of the most common symptoms of depression is fatigue, again for no apparent reason. Someone who has just run the Boston Marathon should expect to feel tired, perhaps for as long as a month afterwards. But if your lifestyle has *not* changed significantly and you are *always* tired, depression may be the reason. Your language may give you away: watch for expressions like *washed up, worn out, dragged down,* or *burnt-out* in your thoughts and conversations about yourself.

- *Chronic headaches, stomach aches, diarrhoea, skin problems, chest pains.* Your family doctor should be the one to decide if you need x-rays, blood tests, eye examinations, cardiograms or other tests, but if your doctor can find no cause for recurring minor ailments, he or she may be looking in the wrong place.

- *Mood swings.* Friends and family are often the first to notice the changeable emotions associated with depression. They complain, "You can never tell how she'll be feeling," or, "He's up one moment, then down the next." Watch for irritability, frequent explosions of temper or cranky behaviour, especially from someone who used to be calm and easy-going.

- *Thoughts of suicide.* If concrete plans for suicide start forming in your mind and Death takes on the appearance of a welcome visitor, make a special effort to get help now! Every suicide threat should be taken seriously.

- *Feelings of worthlessness, or excessive or inappropriate guilt.* Those with depression often torture themselves for real and imaginary faults; they believe themselves to be useless or inferior compared to the rest of the world.

- *Despair and hopelessness.* Some of us are optimists, some are pessimists. Depression, however, gives new meaning to the word "hopeless," as we are overwhelmed by the sheer awfulness of absolutely everything in life.

Self-diagnosis is a tricky business. The above list is meant as a guide and not as a final and infallible test. Even professionals make mistakes when trying to understand and evaluate their own problems. Please don't rely on advice from friends, magazine articles or books (even this one) if you think you have any health problem whatsoever. The chapters on "Getting Help," page 14, and "Resources," page 31, have practical tips on what to do if you need professional help.

A *few words on* bi-polar disorder
(formerly called "manic-depression")

This less common type of mood disorder involves episodes of *depression* alternating with one or more *manic* phases. That is, the usual symptoms of sadness, tears and so on alternate with a greatly elevated mood. Often those with manic-depression are intensely creative and productive; one recent article reported that a "startling number of . . . high-achieving businesspeople have manic-depression."[5] Certain symptoms associated with the manic phase — stamina for work, brilliance of vision and the ability to take risks — may help artists and leaders to achieve almost superhuman goals; unfortunately, the overwhelming change from one extreme to another can be dangerous. The manic phase may include delusions, extreme agitation, compulsive and frantic activity which can eventually prove severely destructive. Patients sometimes go for days without sleeping. Treatment of *bi-polar disorder* usually involves carefully monitored drug therapy. Lithium is commonly used alone or in combination with other medications. It is especially important for those with this condition to follow their doctors' instructions exactly. Because of limitations of space, this book cannot deal with the manic phase in detail, but all of the information and self-help advice on depression would be equally useful for those with manic-depression. See the Appendix for suggestions for further reading.

---

[5] "The CEO's Disease," *Canadian Business*, March 1996, 26.

A few words on Dysthymia
(pronounced dis-thEYE-mee-a)

Dysthymic disorder or dysthymia is a chronic low-grade depression "characterized by a sustained depressed mood lasting two years or more."[6] As we have seen in the previous pages, those with clinical depression are troubled by five or more symptoms (such as sadness or loss of pleasure, sleep disturbances, feelings of hopelessness, fatigue, loss of appetite) lasting for at least two weeks. With dysthymia, the patient experiences a fewer number of the same symptoms for a longer period of time. The Clarke Institute of Psychiatry believes that this costly psychiatric disorder "casts a pall of sadness over the lives of up to seven percent of Canadians."[7] Patients with dysthymia visit the doctor far more frequently than others; after all, they have been suffering for months, troubled by poor appetite, sleep problems, fatigue, or other physical and mental symptoms. Unfortunately, many doctors don't recognize and then treat the underlying condition. Research shows that dysthymia is often helped by Interpersonal Therapy, a relatively brief form of individual psychotherapy which focuses on the relationship problems (unresolved grief, family tensions, divorce, job loss, retirement, social isolation) which are associated with the depressive mood.

3. Causes of Depression

The human brain is an immensely intricate organ composed of membranes, fluids, fibres, blood vessels and ten billion neurons (nerve cells.) Its own in-house pharmacy produces more than fifty mood-altering chemicals like norepinephrine, dopamine, serotonin and endorphins. As part of the central nervous system, it controls the functioning of every part of the body. It is the greatest organ ever created on this earth. Still, for all its complexity, the brain is a concrete object that can be measured, photographed, x-rayed and tested. We can take a picture of the brain, remove bits of it with surgery, and bombard it with radiation. When we die, it dies too; it becomes simply another thing.

---

[6]   Newsletter from the Clarke Institute of Psychiatry, *The Clarke Connection*, Winter 1996, 4.

[7]   Ibid.

The human mind, however, cannot be treated the same way. Like the soul, it is essentially a mystery. Inasmuch as mind and soul are related, we believe that our mind is in some ways eternal. In this light, it is hard for many of us to imagine that researchers can now photograph the physical components of a memory, an emotion, or a thought. Yet PET (positron emission tomography) scanners are being used to do just that! Scientists have learned that specific parts of the brain are affected by our major emotions. Because of the complexity of the brain and the mysterious reciprocal relation of mind and body, we cannot identify a sole or simple cause for depression. Using a microscope, a laboratory technician can watch the specific bacteria that make us sick with tuberculosis. No one has yet devised a foolproof test to identify a physical cause of depression or its sources in the brain. Still, we know more than we once did about the origins of this common disease of the mind.

Some depressions begin with the sadness and grief that are appropriate to life's losses; then, something mysteriously goes wrong with the recovery process. Time passes, but life does *not* go on, we *don't* bounce back, and things do *not* return to normal. Eventually, friends start hinting that maybe we need help. On the other hand, some depressions are not brought on by any particular situation; out of the blue, they slip into a happy life not marked by loss or grief or struggle. All is going well — there's money in the bank, the kids are doing fine at school, you've just landed an important promotion — but for no apparent reason, you've been down in the dumps for weeks.

Why do some of us, but not all of us, experience depression?

- *Genetic predisposition* is an important factor. People don't inherit depression the way they inherit red hair or blue eyes, but some families tend to experience more depression than others. Researchers have discovered that the risk of developing depression is greater if other family members have suffered it.

- *Chemical imbalances* play a key role physically; for some reason the brain produces diminished levels of some of the neurotransmitters which in turn affect the mind. Anti-depressants, including the newer medications that have received such publicity lately (Prozac, Zoloft and so on), work by specifically targeting some of these imbalances.

- Other researchers, especially psychoanalysts and traditional psychiatrists, also see *unresolved tensions* as an important factor in depression, and look for the roots of today's problems in earlier memories, traumas and experiences.

- Psychologists believe that depression can be caused similarly by *low self-esteem,* the effect of life-long behaviour patterns and negative thought processes.

- *Drugs of all kinds*, including prescription medicines, alcohol and street drugs, may also affect our moods. Every drug without exception has side-effects and these sometimes include depression. An example of a prescription drug that in some instances can cause depression is Propranol (with the trade name *Inderal*), a "beta-blocker" used to treat high blood pressure.

- *Physical problems* such as tumours, rheumatoid arthritis, or thyroid deficiency can also provoke depression.

- *Weather-related sensitivity* (called "Winter Depression" or "Seasonal Affective Disorder" — SAD) is a problem for some people. These sufferers respond well to specific light therapies.

- Newer research also considers the dynamics of our particular *society* to explain the prevalence of depression today.

These causes and indicators of depression are not listed in any particular order; often two or more factors are involved. One cause is not more or less important than another; one type of depression is not more real, more painful, or more worthy of treatment, than another. Similarly, every type of treatment has its place. Each person is unique and each case must be diagnosed and treated individually. Furthermore, even doctors sometimes misunderstand both the causes and symptoms of depression. One woman was told by her gynaecologist that her chronic insomnia and fatigue were signs of an early menopause that should be treated with hormone replacement therapy (HRT). The doctor did not confirm this diagnosis by testing her estrogen levels, so, needless to say, the HRT drugs did nothing to cure the serious and long-lasting depression that was the real problem. Another severely depressed man was advised to step up his fitness programme to fight on-the-job stress; he didn't receive appropriate care until his suicidal fantasies started to become frighteningly real. So if you are not satisfied with treatment or diagnosis, speak up. Be prepared to take some responsibility for your own recovery; studies have shown that sometimes it takes years for a correct diagnosis to be made.[8] Don't be afraid of or intimidated by professionals!

A few words on depression and the elderly

Depression is very common among both elderly men and women. In fact, elderly men have the highest rate of "successful" suicide of any age and sex group. In any long-term care facility, up to ten percent of the residents may be suffering from clinical depression at any point in time. The elderly experience the same debilitating symptoms as those in other age groups: change in appetite, decreased energy, sense of hopelessness and helplessness. Unfortunately, cultural stereotypes sometimes prevent us from recognizing that these symptoms are not part of the normal aging process; we assume that old people have naturally lost some of their interest in outside activities, or tire more easily, or have sleep disturbances. Furthermore, many of today's elderly grew up at a time when "respectable" people were discouraged from discussing or displaying their feelings. Depressed senior citizens may not even recognize their own sadness or other emotional distress; instead they may complain about a variety of physical symptoms such as stomach aches, headaches, constipation. Watch for general, non-specific complaints that "everything" hurts. For some people it appears more acceptable and less threatening to have vague physical problems, rather than a specific psychological disturbance which could pose a threat to lifestyle or independence. Some of the elderly with depression may in fact have an underlying neurological problem, such as stroke or tumour, so, once again, it is important to speak to a trained professional for a proper diagnosis. Everyone, regardless of age, deserves to have the best quality of medical care available. If you have an elderly relative, at home or in an institution, who shows some of the symptoms of depression mentioned throughout

---

[8]   1994-95 Annual Report from the Clarke Institute of Psychiatry.

this book, please contact a doctor who may prescribe medication or other appropriate treatments.[9]

4. *Dramatis Personae*

Jaques in Shakespeare's *As You Like It* claimed that "all the world's a stage, and all the men and women merely players." Shakespeare recognized the dramatic value of certain states of mind: he turned Hamlet into the perfect Elizabethan courtier mired in melancholy; he portrayed Lady Macbeth as driven mad in her obsession and guilt. Just think of the great speeches he wrote for King Lear once the old man had fallen over the edge into insanity! Shakespeare's characters look, sound and act recognizably "crazy," tearing their hair, ranting and raving, and generally behaving in ways that set them apart from everyone else on stage. The following cast of characters, all drawn from real life, provides a different perspective on mental illness, one in which a person can hold down a job, dress respectably and make intelligent conversation most of the time. Because privacy is precious, all names and some details have been changed.

Eleanor, a writer and consultant, seriously injured her back in a car accident; the long process of rehabilitation, let alone the months of pain and suffering, put a severe strain on her home life. Realizing that she was not coping well with the accident, Eleanor saw a psychologist for several months; this helped her mind and spirit to survive until her body was able to recover.

Daniel, a rabbi and social worker, loves a challenge: he started playing squash as part of a fitness programme and ended up with a shelf of club trophies and dozens of new friends! An energetic and dynamic man, he is also a great actor; for years, Daniel hid his severe depression from those around him, until recurring thoughts of suicide finally forced him to get help. Thanks to medication, he is now back in the centre of the action where he belongs.

---

[9]   Michelle West, "Depression Among people in Care Situations," Chapter 13 of *Seniority: In Search of the Best in Nursing Homes and Alternative Care in Canada* (Don Mills: Addison-Wesley Publishers Limited, 1991).

Susan is an executive assistant with both courage and perseverance: she worked long hours of overtime to save enough money to travel around the world for a year, a lifelong dream come true. Her friends loved her vivid letters about backpacking through Thailand, Nepal and India; her apartment is decorated with exquisite souvenirs of her trips. Susan is also manic-depressive, and needs medication to regulate her mood swings; a bottle of Lithium stands on a shelf in the kitchen next to a hand-painted Chinese tea pot.

Andy is a computer wizard at a local publishing company. In winter he cycles to and from work in a jazzy purple ski jacket; in summer he spends his weekends camping and hiking with friends. He also sees a psychiatrist once a week on his lunch hour.

Virginia, a retired teacher blessed with a gentle voice and a large heart, is a gracious host to the friends who gather in her home every Thursday to play bridge. In sharp contrast to these civilized afternoons are her terrible memories of childhood. She lost most of her relatives in the War and needed professional help to live with this loss.

The son of a successful businessman, Leo had a long, sad history of depression and suicide attempts. Nothing seemed to help, including hospitalization. A support group for the severely depressed, plus new medication, finally gave Leo the strength to keep going. Now employed in a construction job that he likes, he recently got married, a remarkable recovery for a young man who had once been overwhelmed by self-hate and despair.

Sister Anne is a popular University professor today; former students are always inviting her to weddings and baptisms. Years ago she experienced a serious breakdown, questioning all aspects of her life, past, present and future; six months of therapy helped put some of her doubts and demons to rest.

Andrea is a well-respected nurse, compassionate and creative. She decided to upgrade her qualifications and went back to university, a reasonable goal considering her intelligence and previous academic successes. One day she found herself no longer able to write, a disaster for a student working on a thesis; she was forced to withdraw from the programme. Devastated by this failure, she turned to traditional psychoanalysis; after extensive counselling she was eventually able to finish her degree.

These eight people are survivors. They have taken different routes through the wilderness of mental illness; some required medication, hospitalization and long-term therapy, while others needed less dramatic support. Their stories are not unique; millions of others just like them are trying, day by day, to make sense of their suffering, all the while going to work, caring for families, living normal lives. Celebrities have spoken openly about their personal experiences: Dick Cavett, Kitty Dukakis, Mike Wallace, Patty Duke and Joan Rivers, among others. All of these people are challenging the stereotypes about depression. God grant us the wisdom to see the human face behind each and every label, diagnosis and statistic.

5. Getting Help

The first step on the road to recovery is often the hardest. Acknowledging that we need help is difficult, especially if we see ourselves as strong leaders whose mission in life is to support and inspire others. With all the weapons in our arsenal of disguise and denial, we resist admitting that we have a problem. Such stonewalling usually leads us to see the source of our troubles anywhere but in ourselves. We are tired because our job is stressful; the job is stressful because the workload is too heavy; the workload is too heavy because our colleagues are incompetent. In fact, we are tired because we have not had a decent night's sleep in four months. Similarly, we may be willing to admit we have a problem, but we distract ourselves from its true nature by treating symptoms, not causes. Again, using the example of fatigue given above, we may try to treat the insomnia with massage, acupuncture, exercise and herbal remedies, experimenting with vitamins, special diets, hypnosis, or tranquillity tanks. Why don't we take that first step, and say to ourselves, "Perhaps I need other kinds of help"?

It is not surprising that the first step is the hardest for many depressed people, already bogged down in hopelessness, unable to concentrate and make decisions, tired and more than a little cranky. It scarcely seems possible that anyone — maybe a perfect stranger — could care about our problems; after all, we don't care enough about ourselves to bathe or eat or sleep. Likewise, those who have been looking at life through dust-coloured glasses never expect that simple cures, effective medications and supportive therapists might be found close to home.

It has been said that a truly depressed person might not have the strength to call for help even if the clinic's telephone number were taped to his or her hand. Often we are helped by some outside catalyst: the intervention of a friend; a chance remark overheard at a party; an insightful book, article, or documentary; the suggestion of a supervisor at work; the interest of a colleague with a similar problem. Sometimes a disaster in our personal lives finally forces us, out of sheer terror, to do something: a terrible argument with a loved one, serious financial or legal problems, or a crisis in the family.

Some people are lucky: they know exactly where to turn, but can't quite find the motivation to make that first appointment. If this is your case, re-read the list of symptoms in Chapter 2; ask yourself honestly if some of these apply to you; then try to imagine what life would be like if you felt enthusiastic, well-rested and content for a change. Remember a time in your life when you felt happy and healthy, then look again at this statistic from the Canadian Mental Health Association: eighty percent of people with depression can be treated successfully. Those are far better odds than the ones in the lottery!

If you do not know how or where to begin, here are some practical suggestions.

Your Family Doctor

In today's medicine, the family doctor has become increasingly important. Often called a *general practitioner* (GP) or *primary care physician* and sometimes working in large medical clinics or family practice centres, your family doctor is the one who is best equipped to make referrals, set up appointments with specialists, suggest courses of treatment, and even prescribe suitable medication for depression. If you do not have a family doctor, you should find one, no matter what your current state of health! The walk-in clinics that are springing up in major centres are not appropriate substitutes; they are excellent after-hours and emergency resources, but everyone — adult, teenager, child — should have a family doctor who keeps records for ongoing care. Ask friends and relatives for suggestions; call your nearest hospital for a reference; ask at your church, synagogue, temple or place of worship for advice.

Counselling and Treatment Centres

In Toronto where I live, a trip through the telephone directory could put me in touch with groups such as *Catholic Family Services of Toronto, Jewish Community Services, Alcoholics Anonymous, Canadian Mental Health Association, Depressive and Manic Depressive Association of Ontario, Mood Disorders Association of Metropolitan Toronto, Suicide-Distress Centre, Clarke Institute of Psychiatry* and countless other resources. In extreme cases, even Directory Assistance (dial "4ll") or Emergency (dial "911") will help; callers are given the telephone number of a local distress centre. More information on this topic can be found in Chapter 11, pages 31-34.

Like starting a new job or moving to a new house, taking the first step is challenging, a little frightening and a lot of work. It means trusting that someone will listen without laughing at your problems or blaming you for having them. "Getting help" takes an initial leap of faith: the belief that recovery is possible because everyone can change. The rest of this book will look at aspects of faith, recovery and change that have helped me and countless others. As you start on this journey of self-discovery, remember: you are not alone!

6. Myths and Misunderstandings

We've come a long way from the ignorance of Shakespeare's time, when the mentally ill were kept on display like wild animals in a cage at the zoo. Those in search of an afternoon's entertainment would visit the asylum of St. Mary of Bethlehem (the source of our word *bedlam*) the way sensation-seekers might visit a side show at a carnival. Nevertheless, in spite of the progress made in the last four hundred years, myths and misunderstandings about all mental illnesses, including depression, still persist.

Myth #1: "Only certain kinds of people get depressed."

Depression can be found everywhere in the world, in cities and on farms, among successful executives and unemployed labourers. It strikes men and women, adults, teenagers, children and the elderly. The stereotype of the neurotic New York artist lying on an analyst's couch for ten years misrepresents the real scope of the problem. Prominent world leaders like Winston Churchill have known depression. Abraham Lincoln, strong-minded realist and successful statesman, wrote, "I am now the most miserable man living. If what I feel were equally distributed to the whole human family, there would not be one cheerful face on earth."[10] Churchill and Lincoln were not weak, lazy failures looking for sympathy for non-existent ills, and neither are others who are depressed.

Myth #2: "Truly religious people shouldn't get depressed."

Likewise, there is no truth to the suggestion that those with a strong faith in a loving Creator will be immune to profound despair and doubt. Many deeply religious men and women have experienced such trials: the Psalmist, perhaps King David himself, lamented, "I am weary with my crying" (Psalm 69); Francis of Assisi shed many tears of doubt and frustration; Teresa of Avila experienced blinding headaches; John of the Cross endured his "dark night of the soul." Furthermore, religious people who expect that prayer alone will keep them well are often left with an unnecessary burden of guilt when they don't feel as cheerful and productive as they think they should.

Myth #3: "Bored and lonely housewives use depression as an excuse."

While it is true that more women experience depression, there are significant numbers of men who suffer exactly the same symptoms and require the same help. Male reluctance to get treatment may affect the statistics somewhat. Furthermore, more men also mask their depression through alcohol or drug use. On the other hand, female hormonal changes, pregnancy and menopause may lead to greater vulnerability and explain

---

[10]   John H. Greist, M.D. and James W. Jefferson, M.D., *Depression and Its Treatment* (New York: Warner Books, 1992), 8.

in part the larger numbers of women who suffer depression. In any case, bored and lonely housewives are not the only women to experience depression: so do active and successful career women who are married, single and widowed, as well as mothers and grandmothers, nurses and nuns, teachers and athletes. For more information on women and depression, see Chapter 10.

Myth #4: "Depression has to be treated with medicine"/"Unless you're taking medicine you're not really depressed."

While many people with depression will certainly benefit from medication (see Chapter 9), every person is unique and every case must be treated individually. Wholesale drug therapy might seem to be a cheap and easy answer to a complex problem, but nothing in life is that simple. All medicines work differently in different patients; every drug, including aspirin and cough syrup, has side effects; every depression has its own specific cause or combination of causes. Sometimes those who are helped by certain drugs, especially if they have experienced a dramatic recovery, are overly enthusiastic about advising friends and relatives to try the same pills. Consult your own doctor for the course of treatment that is most appropriate for you.

Myth #5: "You did something to make yourself sick in the first place"/"You could get better on your own if you really tried."

Today's medical climate has been called "the era of the patient," a time when more and more of us accept responsibility for our own good health. Doctors are no longer seen as godlike magicians; as patients, we recognize our significant role in choosing treatment and doing what we can to get well. However, the other side of this valuable change in attitude is a tendency to "blame the victim." When someone gets sick, we point a finger at lifestyle choices such as chronic stress, poor nutrition, inadequate exercise. This attitude is especially unfair when discussing mental illnesses, many of which have physical or genetic origins. Furthermore, the very nature of depression, with its merry-go-round of helpless and hopeless feelings, makes it difficult for many to recover without professional help. As for "trying harder," how can anyone change a chemical imbalance or undo years of psychological trauma through willpower alone? Most depressed people will be discouraged, not encouraged, by suggestions that they are personally responsible for their own illnesses.

Myth #6: "Exercise, proper nutrition, relaxation training or vitamin therapy are all you need for good health."

The above suggestions could be recommended to every single human being living on this earth. In fact many self-help techniques are useful in coping with depression, but on their own they cannot cure *everything*. Exercise enthusiasts too often promise more than fitness can realistically deliver, as do nutritionists, relaxation experts and vitamin therapists.

Myth #7: "It will go away by itself."

One health care worker[11] describes this myth as the single most dangerous attitude in the treatment of any illness. Yes, many diseases are self-limiting — they eventually improve without treatment — but it is impossible to predict which ones will. Some depressions become profoundly worse without treatment, causing unnecessary suffering both for the patient and for concerned family and friends. There is no moral or medical reason to lose precious months of life to despair, fatigue or insomnia while waiting for depression to go away by itself. Furthermore, evidence clearly shows that if depression has not been adequately treated in the beginning, it is more likely to recur with greater severity later on. And if suicidal thoughts or fantasies are present, act now, and get help immediately.

7. Disguises and Denials

The human mind is wonderfully resourceful at hiding unpleasant thoughts from itself and from the outside world. Depression, a disease which is manifested primarily in unpleasant thoughts, with overtones of failure, weakness and shame, is therefore a prime candidate for disguise and denial. How do some people hide such a potentially devastating illness from themselves or others? Here are a few examples of the disguises and denials that camouflage depression.

First of all, in contrast to those obviously immobilized by fatigue, lethargy, disinterest and sadness, some depressed people appear absolutely normal

---

[11]   With thanks to Kathy McLelland, R.N.

on the surface. They hold interesting jobs, care for their families, are active in community affairs. Their "smiling depression" is hidden under compulsive activity which masks a different reality altogether: the depressed person never sits still long enough for anyone to notice the empty, aching void inside. Meanwhile, anger or resentment builds up and physical symptoms become more pronounced, until an inevitable collapse, explosion or breakdown occurs.

Some lifestyles are ideal for disguising the more overt symptoms of depression. According to our stereotypes, moody and creative artists, writers or actors are expected to keep erratic hours and live eccentric lives, so no one notices an unkempt appearance, poor eating habits or frequent unexplained absences. Likewise, drugs and alcohol may be part of a bohemian lifestyle, so overindulgence and experimentation are often ignored. Journalist John Bentley Mays emphasizes this point in his excellent article on depression, "In the Jaws of the Black Dogs."[12]

Likewise, retired senior citizens are not expected to lead interesting, productive lives, and in fact, society mistakenly encourages them to take it easy during their so-called golden years. Changes in health, increased withdrawal from the community, or lack of interest in regular activities are then brushed off as the inevitable consequences of age, loneliness or boredom. In fact, some of these "deteriorating elderly" are just plain depressed and respond to treatment remarkably well.

These are examples of well-disguised depressions, hidden on all sides. Others are obvious to the outside observer but are vigorously denied by the one who suffers. Sometimes cultural prejudices make it difficult or even impossible to be honest about this illness. Alfredo, a recent immigrant to Canada, was permanently confined to a wheelchair after a construction accident; he withdrew more and more from the world until he became a virtual prisoner in his home. He and his family could understand the value of physical therapy, but they could not accept that emotions sometimes need help too.[13]

---

[12] John Bentley Mays, "In the Jaws of the Black Dogs," in *Saturday Night* (November 1993). This article has been expanded into a book: *In the Jaws of the Black Dogs: A Memoir of Depression* (Toronto: Viking, 1995).

[13] Name and some details have been changed.

Others attribute their problems to a multitude of outside sources: "I'd be a lot happier if only I were married"; "Life would be better if I had more money"; "I'll be all right once I find a new job." We are ashamed to admit that the problem lies within; it's easier to blame an external cause for sadness, fatigue or physical ailments. And make no mistake, there is still shame associated with depression, even among sophisticated, educated professionals. We make jokes about Prozac,[14] tranquillizers and other medications; we use demeaning words like *shrink, nut-case, psycho, loony bin, funny farm* in everyday conversation.

Then there is fear. Rightly or wrongly, some are afraid that acknowledging depression, as with any mental illness, will jeopardize career chances. Others are scared that a doctor will force them to take horrible medicines or send them to hospital, making the cure worse than the disease. We are nervous that the therapist will secretly sneer at our puny problems, relatively insignificant compared to those who are "really sick." Some are concerned that therapy and medication will cost more than they can afford; most of us worry that some unfeeling stranger will pry insensitively into secrets about childhood, sexuality or lifestyle. And worst of all, we are terrified that the neighbours will find out, and then, "What will people think?"

Besides these concerns about fear and shame, many people stop looking for solutions to their problems because they have given up hope. Having already tried countless remedies to "calm their nerves," they no longer expect to be well again. Sometimes one negative encounter with a therapist or medication — the wrong person or drug at the wrong time — makes someone reluctant to try again. Some depressions go underground, masked by more spectacular, easily recognized disturbances such as alcoholism, compulsive gambling or chronic obesity. Others suffering from depression hide behind religion, mistaking their overpowering feelings of shame and inappropriate guilt for true guilt or proper humility.

---

[14] Diana, Princess of Wales, was mockingly called the "Prozac Princess" by unscrupulous tabloids. What kind of public outcry would have followed if she had been criticized for having cancer or diabetes?

The above catalogue of disguises and denials covers a lot of territory because human beings are remarkably inventive when it comes to protecting themselves from pain. It may be painful to live with depression, but it is equally painful to face up to the truth, acknowledge our limitations and then try to change the way we feel. In fact, many depressed people pray for the strength to cope with their treatment! We'll look at these issues of hope and courage in more detail in Part II of this book: "The Gift of Illness."

8. Therapy

The treatment of depression often includes some form of "talk therapy" or *psychotherapy*, alone or in combination with medication. The term *psychotherapy* is derived from ancient Greek, *psycho* meaning "breath" and thus "life," "soul" or "spirit"; *therapy* is the art of healing. As in any art, there are elements that cannot be measured. Psychotherapy, or healing the mind and spirit by talking and listening to a trained professional, can be enormously helpful for a range of problems, but many people are unnecessarily frightened or suspicious of both therapists and the therapeutic process, nervous in the presence of something a little mysterious, something that is truly an art. The following is a brief description of the major types of professional therapists who work with depression and other related problems.

- *Psychiatrists* are medical doctors specializing in diseases of the mind. They are qualified to treat a very broad range of mental illnesses, including depressions of all kinds, schizophrenia and other more serious psychotic ailments. Because of their medical background, they are always aware of the connection between mind and body. They are able to prescribe medication and order medical tests and are often associated with a hospital or clinic.

- Many psychologists have advanced degrees in their fields and may be called "Doctor." Their treatments are especially helpful for those who want to change the chronic negative thinking and low self-esteem that often lead to depression. They cannot prescribe any medication directly. As a rule, they are less interested in a lengthy examination of the childhood origin of our adult problems, focusing instead on today's destructive patterns of behaviour.

- *Psychoanalysts* are often, but not always, medical doctors; some have doctorates in other fields such as philosophy. They see each patient several times a week for a relatively long time (perhaps several years); such treatment demands a serious commitment of time, energy and money. Patients talk about anything and everything in order to integrate unconscious childhood disappointments and traumas into conscious adult acceptance.

- *Social workers* see families and couples, as well as individuals. They use short-term counselling to focus on problems which arise from unsatisfactory social relationships.

- *Pastoral counsellors* affiliated with places of worship and family service agencies are especially sensitive to problems associated with illness, bereavement and other challenges to faith.

- *Psychopharmacologists* are doctors, often psychiatrists, who specialize in the use of drugs to treat mental illnesses, including depression. They may work primarily in research, or may be part of a team with other doctors, acting as consultants on medication for those who perform psychotherapy.

- *General practice psychotherapists* are specialized family doctors who treat a range of mind/body ailments such as depression, eating disorders, compulsions and addictions.

- *Psychiatric nurses* likewise offer counselling for mind/body ailments, often leading support and therapy groups.

Therapy can be conducted one-on-one or in groups:

- In *group therapy*, usually led by a professional facilitator, small numbers of people with similar problems meet regularly, usually once a week. A group has some of the same dynamics as a family, so talking, interacting and learning to work in a group helps participants to put aside old, unhealthy patterns of relating in order to grow and eventually to recover.

- *Support groups*, often without a leader, provide an opportunity for those with similar problems to meet regularly for advice and mutual encouragement. They are invaluable in communities where medical or psychotherapeutic resources are limited.

Within every therapeutic discipline, there are other subdivisions and specialities — psychiatrists and psychoanalysts who are especially interested in the theories of Sigmund Freud, Carl Jung, Karen Horney[15] and other thinkers; psychologists who specialize in children's problems, including learning disabilities; pastoral counsellors who practise family mediation and marital counselling; or social workers who perform accident assessments and rehabilitation counselling for insurance companies.

Even for those who require short-term counselling only, finding the right therapist can be a challenge in itself. Because therapy means working face-to-face with another human being, issues of personality, style and temperament are important. It is perfectly possible to have a successful gall-bladder operation performed by a surgeon whom one actively dislikes. It is considerably more difficult to engage in successful therapy when the two parties do not have mutual respect, sympathy and even affection for one another. Be prepared to give the therapist a chance — don't make up your mind after just one visit — but if you still feel uncomfortable or doubtful after several sessions, or if you sense that the therapist is the wrong person for you, don't be afraid to look for someone else.

Therapy by its very nature implies an intimacy that many find frightening. Spouses may resent a stranger learning about sensitive family issues; relatives may fear that the patient, in getting better, will grow away from them. Others worry that they will be blamed for the problems that initiated the therapy in the first place! The patient, too, may have serious reservations about the prospect of change. Reluctant patients, especially if they have been coerced into therapy by someone else, may quietly decide to keep certain aspects of their life off-limits. They will talk for hours but never come close to the real issues that trouble them. For a truly successful therapeutic relationship to develop, patients have to make a serious commitment to honesty and openness. Alert patients who are willing to change soon recognize the issues that really trouble them: the embarrassing or painful memories, thoughts, feelings or dreams that they would just as soon bury or forget. With experience they also know that a

---

[15]   Karen Horney founded the American Institute of Psychoanalysis in 1941.

good therapist will listen to these embarrassing or painful revelations with respect and sympathy, making the process of change a little easier. Over time, talking to someone who keeps on listening "no matter what" has a healing effect. The support and acceptance of the therapist inspires the process of self-acceptance needed by the troubled mind.

9. Medication

Many people who suffer from mood disorders of all kinds will benefit from medication. Dozens of anti-depressants, mood-stabilizers, tranquillizers and sleeping pills are used alone or in combination to treat both the causes and the symptoms of depression. In the media or in conversation with friends, we often hear names like *Fluoxetine* (Prozac), *Sertraline* (Zoloft), *tricyclic antidepressants, monoamine oxidase inhibitors* (MAOIs), tranquillizers (anti-anxiety drugs such as Valium, Librium, Xanax), and *Lithium.* The following suggestions may be helpful for those of you who take medication at some point in your treatment.

- *Ask your doctor or pharmacist for the name, the dosage and the possible side-effects of the medication.* Find out if there are any specific instructions (for example: take with food, between meals, at bedtime) and if there are foods or other drugs you should avoid (milk, alcohol, cough and cold preparations). *If this information is not provided in writing, write it down!* A significant number of patients forget these important details before ever leaving the office or pharmacy.

- *Follow the doctor's instructions exactly!* This may seem obvious, but many people have unspoken reservations about using drugs in the first place and will try to reduce the dosage or stop the medication entirely as soon as they start feeling better. We now use the term "non-compliance" to describe the problem of those who take medicines incorrectly. In fact, fifty percent of all prescription drugs are misused in some way, draining billions of dollars from our health care system.[16] What is non-compliance? This "behavioural disease" includes: not filling or not taking a prescription at all; taking too small or too large a dose; taking

---

[16] From a study by the Pharmaceutical Manufacturers' Association of Canada.

erratic doses; stopping before the prescription runs out; taking medication with alcohol; taking medication without a prescription; and combining the medicine with other drugs.[17]

- Some of those who need long-term treatment with anti-depressants stop taking their medicine because they don't want the drugs to become a "crutch." It is more positive to compare anti-depressants to insulin or to medication used to control high blood pressure. *Prescription medications should be considered tools*, not signs of weakness.

- Many anti-depressants don't start working immediately but need time (up to six weeks) to take effect. *Be patient,* and if you have any concerns, speak to your doctor. Those who joke about rushing out of a stressful meeting to "pop a Prozac" have a naive understanding of the way anti-depressants operate in the body.

- *Be prepared for the side-effects* which are part of every medicine ever invented; even old-fashioned aspirin can cause stomach problems. Common side-effects include dry mouth, weight gain, nausea, mild constipation, dizziness and sleepiness. Some of these can be minimized by changing the time of day when the medicine is taken. If the cure starts to be worse than the disease, ask your doctor about other possibilities. Sometimes it takes a little experimentation to find the right drug and dosage. Many of the newer medications have milder side-effects, accounting in part for their popularity.

- Anti-depressants are not pep pills or "uppers." They have no effect on someone who is not depressed; they are not addictive; many people will need them for a short time only. If you are reluctant to take medication in general, *give the treatment a fair chance* for several weeks, and then discuss the situation again with your doctor or therapist.

---

[17] From *The Health Journal* (December 1995), 20.

A few words about electro-convulsive therapy (ECT)

Commonly called "shock therapy" or "shock treatment," this procedure is sometimes used in severe cases of depression and other mental illnesses that have not responded to medication or other treatments. Performed in a hospital under general anaesthetic, ECT is not a horrifying experience as is commonly thought; rather, after ECT most patients experience dramatic improvement when all else has failed them. Patients feel no pain, and have no memory of the treatment. In the past some patients worried about memory loss after repeated ECTs, but newer techniques have substantially reduced this concern.

10. Especially for Women

As we have seen, statistics show that more women than men experience depression: one woman in four can expect to suffer from depression at some point in her life. While recognizing that depression also affects significant numbers of men, let's look at some of the factors that influence women's health, physical and mental.

Biological Factors

Women can climb mountains, fix engines, run marathons and win court cases exactly like their brothers, fathers and uncles, but only women can bear children. Women's bodies have evolved to facilitate the conception, gestation (pregnancy) and birth of children, and to do this women's bodies produce specific female hormones through glands which then regulate organs and cycles of life — more chemicals washing through the brain and influencing the mind! Various events in the course of a woman's life — puberty, regular menstruation, pregnancy and childbirth (if they occur), and menopause — can affect us both physically and mentally.

Many women say that their moods are substantially different before, during and after menstruation. Those who suffer from difficult periods become acutely aware of the regular presence of pain in their lives; subsequently they may come to fear and hate their bodies, the source of the pain. One condition that is receiving a lot of publicity lately is *Pre-Menstrual Syndrome* (PMS), whose symptoms include extreme nervousness, bloating, food cravings and fatigue in the days before menstruation begins. Doctors and women themselves differ in their evaluation of this condition. Researchers have recently discovered that Prozac, one of the common anti-depressants, can help PMS. Is PMS, therefore, a type of depression caused by hormonal changes, or is the depression already present, affecting a woman's ability to cope with what is in fact a normal biological process? Unsympathetic observers ask, "Does PMS even exist or is it just a trendy pseudo-ailment?" There are arguments on all sides, and we need better answers to these questions.

Likewise, menopause and its changes are further sources of stress, and menopause management is also under review, with much controversy raging over the value of *Hormone Replacement Therapy* (HRT). As menstruation comes to an end, some women experience severe mental strain caused by impaired memory, fatigue, mood swings and insomnia — symptoms similar to depression. Furthermore, phrases like the "change of life" imply more than just biological change; some women feel that menopause signals the end of useful life, a good enough reason to feel depressed. The controversy over HRT in part mirrors our concern for interfering with the normal process of aging and our worries about the risks involved in the long-term use of medication. The debate also reflects our uncertainty about the ways in which physical and mental states interact. How do we treat one without the other?

Again, pregnancy and childbirth put strong stresses and strains on all aspects of a woman, including the mind. One out of ten women, for example, experiences some post-partum depression after childbirth, in some cases developing true clinical depression.[18] Is this a reasonable reaction to hormone fluctuations, extreme fatigue or physical stress, or is it caused by other emotional factors? A woman's risk of post-partum depression is increased if she lives far away from her family, or if none of her close relatives are with her at the time of birth. Is this, then, a mental or physical disorder? As in all the other examples, we are left with many questions about the relationship between body and mind.

---

[18] According to Depression After Delivery, an American organization dedicated to helping new mothers and educating professionals.

Cultural and Social Factors

Other observers emphasize the role played by cultural and social pressures on women. The traditional view of society implied that women should be the nurturers and men the breadwinners. Women's roles have changed significantly in the last forty years, but confusion about those roles has left some women vulnerable to depression. Single or childless women with no one to nurture may still receive subtle signals that they are incomplete, unfulfilled, unfeminine; at the same time, mothers who work may feel guilty about being away from home and family. (In a similar way, unemployed or retired men may fear that they will lose their masculinity when they stop being the family breadwinners.)

Women have had to battle long and hard for the right to vote, to work, and to study; women have had to fight to live on equal terms before the law as men do. In spite of great advances in equality in Western society, the rest of the world has not caught up yet, and even here at home many women do not experience equal respect and opportunity. Statistics show that women generally shoulder most of the burden for child care and domestic duties, the "second shift" of never-ending work that often contributes to stress and fatigue. Thus some commentators say that women's depressions and other mental problems are environmentally induced, a reasonable reaction to the unreasonable circumstances of discrimination and oppression under which women often live.

Many women grew up in families where fathers and brothers were valued more than mothers and daughters. Girls were taught that being nice — quiet, well-behaved, deferential, neat, controlled — was more important than being creative, independent, resourceful or successful. They were encouraged to put others' needs first. They grew up expecting to earn less, to achieve less, to have a less important role in society and the family. These negative attitudes and expectations can affect a woman's mental health. The American Psychological Association suggests that women tend to "brood and dwell on their problems" compared to men who are "more likely to employ action and mastery strategies." Furthermore, "women who are more passive, dependent, pessimistic or negative in their attitudes are more likely to become depressed, particularly if they dwell on their bad feelings." Other risk factors that affect women are sexual or physical abuse, poverty, minority status and family circumstances. As the APA notes, "mothers of young children are very vulnerable to depression, and the more children a woman has, the more likely it is that she'll be depressed."[19]

Many women have good reason to complain about the doors that are closed to them throughout life. A woman who looks back on the subtle or blatant discrimination of her youth, resenting and regretting a lifetime of lost opportunities, may well find that she is especially vulnerable to depression, one fed by a culturally conditioned self-image and further affected by hormonal changes and physical stress.

Women's Strengths

Thus, for a combination of physical and cultural reasons, women are more susceptible to depression; at the same time, they have certain strengths that help them cope differently than men. In general, women are more willing to accept counselling as an answer; they speak more freely about their problems and are more likely to join support groups. They are less likely to use alcohol or drugs which both mask and exacerbate mental problems. They are exposed to more information on depression and related problems through women's magazines and family publications. Because they often see a doctor regularly — for pregnancy, child care, regular PAP smears or breast examinations — they are usually familiar with the health care system.

A Plea for Tolerance

Anyone who is not part of the mainstream of society — for example, racial minorities or the physically challenged — may experience some of the same cultural causes for depression as women. A just and equitable society with equal opportunities for all would recognize our similarities while allowing us to protect our unique and important differences. Rock singer Bruce Springsteen, who often celebrates the struggles and victories of the ordinary person in his songs, is fond of saying, "No one wins unless we all win." This is especially true when society considers its collective mental health.

---

[19] From *What You Should Know About Women and Depression,* a brochure from the American Psychological Association.

11. Resources

The Canadian Mental Health Association (CMHA) maintains over one hundred offices across the country. The provincial division offices are listed below; call for information on your community.

National Office
2160 Yonge Street, 3rd Floor
Toronto, ON M4S 2Z3
(416) 484-7750

Alberta Division
328 Capital Place
9707-110th Street
Edmonton, AB T5K 2L9
(403) 482-6576

British Columbia Division
#1200 - 1111 Melville Street
Vancouver, B.C. V6E 3V6
(604) 688-3234

Manitoba Division
2-836 Ellice Avenue
Winnipeg, MB R3G 0C2
(204) 775-8888

New Brunswick Division
65 rue Brunswick
Fredericton, NB E3B 1G5
(506) 455-5231

Newfoundland Division
P.O. Box 5788
St. John's, NF A1C 5X3
(709) 753-8550

Northwest Territories Division
PO Box 2580
Yellowknife, NT X1A 2P9
(403) 873-3190

Nova Scotia Division
63 King Street
Dartmouth, NS B2Y 2R7
(902) 466-6600

Ontario Division
180 Dundas Street West
Suite 2301
Toronto, ON M5G 1Z8
(416) 977-5580

Metropolitan Toronto Branch
970 Lawrence Avenue West, Suite 205
Toronto, ON M6A 3B6
(416) 789-7957

Prince Edward Island Division
170 Fitzroy Street, P.O. Box 785
Charlottetown, PE C1A 7L9
(902) 566-3034

Quebec Division
550 Sherbrooke Street West, Suite 310
Montreal, PQ H3A 1B9
(514) 849-3291

Saskatchewan Division
2702 - 12th Avenue
Regina, SK S4T 1J2
(306) 525-5601

Yukon Division
6 Bates Crescent
Whitehorse, YT Y1A 4T8
(403) 668-8812

Other Resources in Ontario:

D.I.R.E.C.T. (Depression Resource and Education Centre-Toll-free: telephone line with detailed recorded messages about depression and manic-depressive illnesses: in Ontario, 1-888-557-5051, extension 8000.

Mood Disorders Association of Metropolitan Toronto
40 Orchard View Boulevard
Suite 222
Toronto, ON M4R 1B9
(416) 486-8046
(includes library, bookstore and resource material as well as referrals, support groups and newsletter.)

Depressive & Manic Depressive Association of Ontario
214 Merton Street
Suite 101
Toronto, ON M4S 1A6
(416) 943-0434

Depression/Manic Depression Mutual Support Group of Ottawa
1355 Bank Street
Suite 402
Ottawa, ON K1H 8K7
(613) 737-7791

Ontario Psychological Association
for referrals to psychologists:
(416) 961-0069

Depression and Manic-Depression Association for Waterloo Region
20 Erb Street West
11th Floor, Marsland Centre
Waterloo, ON N2L 1T2
(519) 884-5455

Manic Depressive Association for the Region of Peel
150 Clark Boulevard
Suite 87
Brampton, ON L6T 4Y8
(905) 455-9366

Hamilton Depressive and Manic Depressive Support & Education Group
c/o East Region Mental Health Services
2757 King Street East
Hamilton, ON L8G 5E4
(905) 573-4801

Bi-Polar Affective Disorders Support Group
Hotel Dieu Hospital
Kingston, ON
(613) 544-3310

Durham Region Manic-Depressive and Depressive Self-Help Group
275 Ormond Drive, Unit 46
Oshawa, ON L1K 1S1

Windsor Mood Disorders
Box 2241, Walkerville
Windsor, ON N8Y 4R8
(519) 254-7357

Other Resources:

Many other regions have similar associations. A selection is listed below; for further information on your area, call the Canadian Mental Health Association or look in the Yellow Pages.

Mood Disorders Association of British Columbia
2730 Commercial Drive
Suite 201
Vancouver, BC V5N 5P4
(604) 873-0103

Society for Depression and Manic-Depression of Manitoba
4-1000 Notre Dame Avenue
Winnipeg, MB R3E 0N3
(204) 786-0987

Manic-Depressive Association of Greater Vancouver
P.O. Box 35582
Vancouver, BC V6M 4G9
(604) 253-6560

Manic-Depressive Support Group
Lasalle Psychiatric Centre
8630 Centrale
Lasalle, PQ H8P 1N5

Depressive and Manic-Depressive Association, Quebec Alliance
5253 Decarie Blvd, Suite 150
Montreal, PQ H3W 3C3
(514) 486-1448

Other National Resources:

Social Work Department
Clarke Institute of Psychiatry
250 College Street
Toronto, Ontario M5T 1R8
(416) 979-2221, ext. 2576
(booklets available)

Canadian Psychiatric Association
Suite 200
237 Argyle
Ottawa, Ontario K2P 1B8
(613) 234-2815

Depression and Manic-Depression Association of Canada
4-1000 Notre Dame Avenue
Winnipeg, MB R3E 0N3
(204) 786-0987

Prozac hot-line for doctors and pharmacists only: 1-800-663-3363. Open twenty-four hours a day.

Sleep/Wake Disorders Canada hot-line: 1-800-387-9253, a national self-help support group.

For information on drug and alcohol dependency, see Chapter 27; for anorexia and bulimia, see Chapter 41.

Suggestions for using the telephone directory: look in the Yellow Pages under Marriage, Family and Individual Counsellors; Mental Health Services; Psychologists; Psychotherapy; Social Service Organizations; Stress Management and Counselling; Women's Organizations and Services.

Part II

The Gift of Illness

... the spiritual dimension of illness and suffering ...

12. The Gift of Illness

It's Christmas morning and I am twelve years old. Underneath the big Douglas fir that reaches to the living room ceiling are piles of wonderful presents: puzzles and games, sweaters and scarves, books and hockey sticks, all wrapped in beautiful paper and decorated with ribbons and bows. In a flurry of excitement, we open our gifts right after breakfast, then hurry off to church for Christmas morning mass. Later on in the course of the day, Auntie Marion and Uncle Buck come over for a visit. Auntie Marion gives each of us a present, and in her old-fashioned way says, "Santa Claus left these for you at my house." As usual she brings us pairs of the expertly crafted mittens which she knits every year for her many nieces and nephews. Unfortunately, this year mine are battleship grey with navy blue stripes, not at all like the pretty pink and white ones I would have chosen. A little disappointed but mindful of my manners, I thank my dear aunt, a gentle woman with thinning hair and tired eyes. When she dies ten years later I remember her kindness; needless to say, I am still wearing the mittens. When they finally fall apart long after my university graduation, it is surprisingly hard to part with them. They have become an almost perfect gift.

We rarely choose the gifts that are waiting for us under the great Christmas tree of Life. Children look for frilly blouses and the latest toys and sometimes they find socks and underwear instead. Adults hope for diamond rings and new cars and discover ironing boards and snow shovels! Plainly speaking, we ask for health, happiness and success in life, and sometimes we receive illness, sorrow and disappointment. But, like the mittens in their ordinary cardboard boxes, time sometimes reveals an unexpected usefulness to these gifts.

Illness and Auntie Marion's mittens have something in common. No one would willingly choose illness; every human impulse warns us that here is something to be avoided at all cost. As people of faith we may be especially troubled by this strange gift. During the experience of an illness like depression, when life feels bleak, forlorn and empty, it seems that all traces of God's presence have disappeared from the world. Like the author of Psalm 22, we may be horrified by this experience, calling out, "My God, my God, why have you forsaken me?" If you have struggled to understand the apparent meaninglessness of depression, you may be shocked by the suggestion that illness can be a gift. I invite you to come with me on a search for meaning.

Let's begin with one simple question: "What is a gift?" Looking for a simple answer, we recognize first of all that the privilege of choosing the gift usually belongs to the giver. Applying this to the origin of illness, faith tells us that God has "chosen" the gift. That is, the God who loves us has allowed depression (or heart disease or diabetes) to exist for some reason. Honesty compels me to add that illness can often be a test of this faith. Is our belief in a loving Creator dependent upon our current state of health and happiness? Can we accept that God will be present in the painful realities of life? Like so many of the most profound aspects of human life, suffering is touched with mystery, potentially transforming, sometimes elusive, and ultimately linked to the great Mystery that is God.

Secondly, we don't normally receive gifts from strangers. A gift is both a symbol and an expression of personal love; thus the gift of illness reinforces a bond that *already* exists between the One who gives and the one who receives. We are all children of God whether we recognize it or not. Illness gives us a unique opportunity to change, to deepen or to re-evaluate our relationship with our Creator. By forcing us to recognize our vulnerability and our limitations, illness invites us to dwell for a few moments in the shadow of Eternity.

Finally, the choice of the gift reflects the perception of the giver. Receiving the gift of illness, we often cry out, "Why me? Why now?" God's infinite wisdom gently replies, "Because I know you need this today." God does not hand out sickness with a malicious gleam in a vindictive divine eye. And what I may call "random suffering" is not random at all. I may need to spend long periods in prayer, meditation and reflection, struggling with my disappointments, anger and confusion, before I can understand and then accept the pattern of my life. But each personal experience of illness has a unique importance for each individual life.

Wandering around in the turmoil of spirit that is depression, most of us will hardly notice any positive aspects to illness. We can't see any value in fatigue, tears, insomnia; we certainly would not have picked out this so-called gift for ourselves, yet Providence has permitted this event in our lives. We believe that God knows and loves this creation, while seeing the shape of each human life much more clearly than we can. How do we reconcile the tension between our very real suffering and this belief in a loving God?

When faith is challenged by illness, we may be tempted to take refuge in cynicism or bitterness. Let's return to the childlike example of the mittens. How did I ever learn to appreciate them? At first, I stuffed the box in the bottom of a drawer; later that winter, when all my other mittens were missing-in-action, I took another look. Maybe they weren't so bad after all. After a couple of hours playing in the snow, I discovered their hidden qualities: warm, waterproof, almost indestructible! In time I barely noticed the boring colours. In the same way I can appreciate even the hidden qualities of depression, another unlikely gift "chosen" just for me, once I am ready to look more closely at the meaning of my experience.

In Part II of this book we will examine various aspects of the gift of illness, the surprising ways that depression can change our attitudes and deepen our spiritual lives. Depression may be caused by a combination of subtle changes in hormones and brain cells interacting with the specific ups and downs of my unique life history; as we saw in Part I, it is a disease that can and should be treated medically. At the same time, people of faith can recognize that depression, like all other diseases, is allowed to exist in this still imperfect world by our loving Creator. No suffering is ultimately meaningless; there is only suffering that is apparently meaningless for us now. On our journey through the wasteland of illness, many of us will discover that God can indeed make the desert blossom. Such a miracle is hard to imagine when I'm down in the dumps and sadness makes it hard to be grateful for *anything*. God speed the day when the real meaning of depression will be clear to me, and I can truly give thanks for my experience of this surprising and unlikely gift.

13. The God of Surprises

Human beings are curious: we like to know how things work! When researchers start to explore an illness like depression they look for causes and explanations; they study facts and figures, statistics and case histories in order to make sense of the suffering that affects so many of us. While it is important to understand the medical origins for depression, our spiritual beliefs remind us of other important dimensions as well.

Even if we recognize that God has permitted an illness to occur, we may still be puzzled by this *unexpected* black cloud on the horizon of a healthy life. As suggested in the last chapter, we ask, "Why me? Why now? Things were going along so well; I just can't understand how this happened!" One wise retreat director suggests that we look to "the God of Surprises" for an answer.[1] He explains that our loving Creator is ultimately the source for these unexpected interruptions in the course of life, the apparently illogical twists and turns of fate that we cannot readily understand or accept.

Look at history, your own and everyone else's: often there are enough twists and turns in life to satisfy anyone's thirst for high drama. Tragedies turn into constructive turning-points, windfalls are really millstones in disguise. No one can predict the future, not everything is what it appears to be, and truth can be stranger than fiction! We can deduce from statistics that many of us will receive the gift of illness in this life; many of us will

---

[1]   With thanks to Roger Bonneau, O.Carm., Director of Mount Carmel Spiritual Centre, Niagara Falls, Ontario, for bringing Gerard W. Hughes' book, *The God of Surprises* (Toronto: Anglican Book Centre, 1985), to my attention.

also discover that sickness and suffering can have unexpected benefits, the *surprising*, positive side-effects that we least expect to find.

Illness sometimes gives this unexpected gift: the gift of *time*, time to think, to wonder, to remember, to understand. The gift of time can cause profound changes in our attitudes and lifestyles as we re-evaluate both past and future in the light of present problems. Ignatius Loyola, the founder of the Jesuits, and Francis of Assisi, founder of the Franciscans, experienced life-changing conversions — from soldiers to major religious leaders — after recuperating from serious injuries. Anthony Burgess began his prolific writing career after being diagnosed (incorrectly as it turned out) with a terminal illness. Personally, I experienced a surprising upheaval in my life because of illness. On my fortieth birthday, I started taking medication for endometriosis;[2] within weeks I was forced to cut back on my usual work because the hormone treatments left me nauseated, dizzy and depressed. Staying home for a few extra hours a day caused a remarkable creative explosion in my life: I started writing on a regular basis to distract myself from the side-effects of the medication. During the long and discouraging months of treatment I had lots of time to tackle a demanding literary project that had always interested me. This research formed the basis for my first book. Was illness a positive or negative event in these three lives?

We can even be changed by the illnesses of others; one of my friends recalls nursing her widowed brother during his last few months with lung cancer: "I did as much as I could; it was my final gift to him. He would brighten up when he saw me there in the kitchen, waiting to make his breakfast. The jokes we shared every morning brought a smile to his face for the whole day. Helping him enjoy life until the end was one of the most powerful experiences of my whole life." Through illness, this woman learned a lesson of compassion and perseverance which she will never forget.

Does anyone ever learn anything from the gift of health? Until we experience a taste of illness, we blithely wend our way through life,

---

2   Endometriosis is a condition in which tissue lining the uterus is found in other areas of the body, causing pain and often infertility. Today it is frequently treated with laser surgery.

41

expecting strength, energy and enthusiasm to continue day after day. The blessings of good health, a strong constitution and a naturally cheerful disposition are so easily ignored, especially when we are young. Unfortunately, most of us do not understand, value or even notice the gift of health until we suddenly find that it has disappeared.[3]

On the other hand, those who have coped with illnesses of all kinds tell a different story. After confronting their own vulnerability, they no longer take the future for granted; life suddenly seems far more precious when it has been threatened in any way. Yes, illness sometimes makes us bad-tempered, impatient, resentful. And "being sick" is not more noble than "getting well again." The advances of medicine and our own ability to recover are great gifts worth celebrating. But surprising as it may seem, most of us feel we are better people for having lived for a while in the shadow of ill-health.

Coping with struggles of any description can inspire much spiritual growth. Illness teaches us to treasure every moment with family and friends; hobbies and recreation no longer take a back seat to work and career; financial success and public recognition aren't as important as they once were. Illness can open our eyes to the simple pleasures of everyday life, as opposed to the empty and expensive diversions we sometimes substitute for living. Illness hints that there might be a better way to spend the rest of our days. As one woman said after the tragic suicide of her son, "The dark night of the soul is a great passage to other illuminations."[4] Through illness and suffering, the God of Surprises has given us a powerful, poignant opportunity to change and grow.

14. The Meaning of Suffering

Margaret's mother died in the spring after a long and painful battle with cancer. Her father had passed away a few years' previously; neither of her parents lived to be 70. Margaret tried to be brave and philosophical about these deaths, so a few months later she and her husband Donald decided to take a much-needed vacation in Scotland. While visiting relatives near Inverness, Donald was killed in a car accident; Margaret

---

[3] With thanks to Ellen Asher for this idea.

[4] Singer and writer Judy Collins in *You* magazine, August 1995.

was four months pregnant at the time. One silent, anguished thought passed through the minds of everyone who heard the terrible news: "How can God allow such things to happen?"[5]

If there is a God, a loving God who cares about our world, why is there so much suffering in this life? If you have been around awhile, you could substitute another example of horrendous tragedy for this true story about Margaret and Donald. What can be the purpose of these events? In the past, people often interpreted tragedy and suffering as divine retribution for human wickedness, both individual and collective. Horrible as this vision of God, the punishing judge, might be, it could sometimes make sense of the sadness of life. Finding an explanation for "needless suffering" is more complicated when our prayers are directed to God, the Good Shepherd, and Jesus, our loving friend.

Those who have lived through terrible tragedy admit that they soon tire of the platitudes offered by tongue-tied friends sincerely trying to help. How true! Most of us can't find many eloquent words of comfort while visiting a funeral home or sitting by a hospital bed. In fact, a whole shelf-load of books, let alone one humble chapter, would not be enough to explain the meaning of suffering. But one thing I have learned from my own experiences: a story of suffering is not told quickly or easily. Rather, it is a long, slow *process* composed of many different moments and moods, light and shade, sunshine and shadow. Even in the midst of the deepest sadness, there can be laughter beside the tears. Right after a death, those who mourn are often surprised to find themselves smiling at a joke or enjoying a meal; they expected suffering to be a monolithic slab of pain, unchanged and everlasting. Instead, there are tiny pinpricks of light, small, insignificant experiences of peace, hope or comfort, the first signs that happiness might one day return. These brighter moments can show us the way through the darkness and into the daylight.

Furthermore, the lengthy and varied process of suffering seems to fill some important role in the lifelong development of each person. Struggling within our humanity, we try to make sense of our sorrow by thinking, reflecting, musing, wishing, praying, bargaining, or dreaming. Then, because of those odd glimmers of light in the darkness, we are

---

[5]   Names and some details have been changed.

often inspired to look towards the future for something better — for recovery, for acceptance, for reconciliation. We begin to search for tools that will help us cope. Thus the meaning of suffering changes moment by moment, even as we are changed by the experience.

A wise young woman[6] told me a story to illustrate the meaning of suffering: she said that life is like a huge, hand-made quilt. From our limited perspective here in the present, we see the broken threads and the uneven stitches, the marks of the needle, a few stains and wrinkles, a little hole here and there. Indeed we can't really understand anything of the complicated pattern of colour and design; all we see are the dozens of different fabrics, the thousands of tiny stitches. But far away where God sits in eternity, the meaning and beauty of the quilt look very different. When we suffer intensely, we see only too clearly the piece of thread that is broken, and this is normal and good; no reasonable person expects us to cope with pain by pretending that it does not exist. But as we move closer towards God through reflection, prayer and faith, we can see more and more of the quilt, more and more of the pattern.

When we are depressed, it is very easy to notice only the broken threads; feeling hopeless and helpless, we dwell on the very real sadness around us, obsessed with the greyness and gloom of life. We rage, fight, deny and rebel, arguing over and over about the meaning of suffering, never finding peace. We collect stories like the one about Margaret and Donald, then file them away in a great mental storeroom labelled "Darkness and Despair." "How can God allow this to happen?" becomes the refrain of a favourite lament. We don't even hope for an answer, remembering that philosophers and sceptics have asked this same question for centuries. We don't look for the pattern, we see only the problem, the broken thread.

When I am confronted by the large and small tragedies of life, including my own moments of sadness and discouragement, I try to focus instead on another question, one that recognizes my own suffering, does not trivialize my struggles, and still acknowledges the will of my all-powerful and ever-mysterious Creator. With whatever humility is in my heart, I pray: "Dear God, what would you have me learn from this experience?"

---

[6]   With thanks to Christianne Martin.

15. Humility

One relaxed summer evening at a barbecue, two middle-aged women[7] had a long heart-to-heart talk, laughing and crying about the headaches and satisfactions of their respective lives. Linda confided that she was having problems with her teenage children; Kate shyly confessed that she had been seeing a doctor for depression. Intensely ashamed of needing a psychiatrist, she had never before talked about her weekly therapy except to her immediate family and a few colleagues at work. To Kate's surprise, her friend turned to her and snapped, "What do *you* have to feel depressed about?" Deeply humiliated by this reaction, Kate kept her depression and its treatment a secret for many more months.

Humility is very often confused with humiliation. As an attempt to punish or repress, humiliation consists of words and actions which attack our dignity and self-esteem. Sometimes intended as humour or harmless teasing, humiliating acts poke fun at common weaknesses, failures and disabilities. Humiliation creates embarrassment, fear and shame by making the victim feel less than human, all because he or she is less than perfect. This is what Linda unwittingly did: she made the unfair assumption that Kate's satisfying career and happy home life would automatically prevent her from feeling unhappy or depressed.

Humility is another matter entirely; a much misunderstood virtue, humility has nothing to do with embarrassment, fear, shame or laughter. It is *not* weak submissiveness or false modesty. The word "humility" is derived from the Latin *humus*, meaning "ground, earth, soil." Today "humus" is a rich growing medium formed by the slow decomposition of organic matters. Gardeners treasure this nutrient-rich soil, just as we can treasure humility, formed when fear, arrogance and false pride have begun to decompose, to be replaced by courage, honesty and openness, the ground where other virtues can take root and grow. In spite of popular misconceptions, humility does *not* mean thinking poorly of oneself. C. S. Lewis in *The Screwtape Letters* rightly describes the "element of dishonesty and make-believe" that is so often mistaken for this useful virtue: the beautiful who pretend to be ugly and the clever who pretend

---

[7]   Names and some details have been changed.

to be stupid. This is light years away from true humility.[8] True humility is not the exaggeration of our faults and the minimizing of our assets, but the acceptance of both strengths and weaknesses honestly.

For anyone suffering from depression, susceptible by the very nature of the disease to feelings of worthlessness and shame, there are plenty of opportunities to feel humiliated. Humility, however, can be enormously liberating. Humility gives me the freedom to make the first telephone call to a doctor, therapist or clinic; it helps me talk openly about my very real problems; it strengthens my courage to follow a course of treatment. Because humility is rooted in honesty, it means making an effort to appreciate my strengths and weaknesses together; it does not mean focusing exclusively and obsessively on the negative aspects of my past or present life and character.

In humility I do everything in my power to know and love my true self. For some of us, that involves learning more about our illness through research; it may mean overcoming shyness and shame to join a support group with others; it might include accepting medication, long-term therapy or even hospitalization as the most appropriate and effective means of dealing with depression. In true humility, I do not run away from my problems, however mild or severe. I do not tell myself that I deserve to be sick because I am such a terrible person, nor do I lament that life will never get better. Anything that dishonestly undermines my acceptance of who I really am, strengths and weaknesses alike, is not humility. Humility rejoices in the presence of a loving God in the events of my life, even if the events include gifts like depression. Humility rejoices when I admit that I cannot do everything on my own, especially make myself well; humility rejoices when I have the courage to ask for help.

16. Learning to Let Go

Coping with depression means learning humility; sometimes self-reliance stands in the way of the lesson. In debunking the myth that depressed people are self-indulgent weaklings, I explained in Chapter 1 that those

---

[8]   C. S. Lewis, *The Screwtape Letters* (Glasgow: Collins, Fount Paperbacks, 1977), Chapter 14.

who suffer from depression are often highly responsible perfectionists. These are the very people who misuse the virtue of self-reliance, turning it from a valuable asset into a potential liability. Those who take life's burdens and obligations too seriously are the ones who have the most trouble *learning to let go*.

Suggestions about learning to let go can be terrifying to those who have devoted a lifetime to holding on tight. Will relaxing our standards, lowering our expectations and putting the past behind us result in disaster, chaos and confusion? Having been coiled up like a gigantic spring for so many years, we can hardly believe that there is another way to live. Those suffering from depression are often advised to "go for help." But before we can derive any benefit from professional care, we must first recognize that indeed we have a problem. Perhaps we start by identifying our symptoms, making a mental checklist of the aspects of life that feel uncomfortable or out-of-balance. The next step is deciding to do something, perhaps call our family doctor. And so it continues. Dr. David Burns describes the process he calls the "paradox of acceptance": we must identify then *accept* our negative thoughts and feelings first, and by doing this, we are ultimately able to overcome them.[9] Thus acknowledging depression may be the first time that some of us have ever asked for help, the first time that we have ever said, "I can't do it all by myself."

Learning to let go often includes developing a healthy, constructive relationship with a doctor, therapist or support group. Talking about our problems requires breaking down the barriers of privacy and detachment, embarrassment and shame, barriers that keep others from getting too close to us. Such a positive step can lead to subsequent improvements in many different areas, including our relationships with family, friends and co-workers. Furthermore, as it becomes easier to share our thoughts and feelings, we can then transfer this new openness to our spiritual lives.

Many of us grew up with religious beliefs and practices that were rigid and repressive, to say the least. We were not taught to pray with any

---

9   David D. Burns, M.D., *The Feeling Good Handbook* (New York: Plume Books, published by the Penguin Group, 1990), 38 *et passim*.

creative spontaneity or imagination; we learned our catechism by heart, memorizing religious history and Bible passages. Most of the time we did not develop any personal relationship with God, especially if we were born before the revolution in religious thought of the 1960s. Almighty God was out there somewhere, vague, slightly scary and infinitely far removed from this world; no one taught us to focus on God down here, personally involved in our lives, concrete and real. Learning to let go can thus help us relate to God as mature, confident adults, turning to our Creator with trust and not fear, from love and not duty alone.

Learning to let go also means seeing the undeniable humour of life, the unexpected and outrageous moments of sublime foolishness that belong to this Divine Comedy of existence. Having a sense of perspective on the ridiculous side of life allows us to laugh when we might otherwise break down in tears. Marion Woodman, noted Jungian analyst and writer, kept an audience in stitches one day talking about the humorous aspects of growing older: rushing to answer the doorbell, but stopping first to put on one's glasses in order to find one's false teeth! Marion's light-hearted anecdote came in the middle of a talk on "Conscious and Creative Living"; she was not afraid to use a little well-timed levity in her discussion of a profoundly serious subject.[10] Learning to let go thus includes learning to say, "My feeble attempts to pretend I am perfect are a waste of time. Who am I trying to fool, anyway?" This morsel of wisdom goes a long way towards erasing the false and foolish pride which stands in the way of humility.

Learning to let go also means giving ourselves time to heal. Many of us are surprised to find that regaining our health takes longer than expected. Our society, too concerned about productivity, unfortunately makes unrealistic assumptions about sickness and recovery; as a result, many of us are ashamed about needing time to heal. Yet taking time for treatment is not an indulgence but a necessity! In the words of one wise and sympathetic psychiatrist, "We are not machines. Sometimes we cannot

---

[10] November 2, 1995, at an address to the Day-Timers' Program of the First Unitarian Congregation of Toronto. I was part of an ensemble that presented a programme of Medieval and Renaissance music at this event.

bounce back after great hurt, pain and sickness, and we should not have to demand this of ourselves."[11]

Learning to let go can thus be an act of enormous liberation on many fronts. Spiritually speaking, it means accepting that God, like a loving father or mother, knows me inside and out. Likewise, learning to let go gives me permission to be wounded and in need of healing, however long this might take. I am allowed to be weak and in need of someone else's strength, including the strength and experience provided by therapy, medication or other treatments. Finally, learning to let go recognizes that I am not alone in my struggles. The loving support of many individuals — doctors, therapists, friends, and ultimately, God my creator — is there whenever I am ready to accept it.

17. Connections

"You are not alone!" These four little words of comfort are the primary message of hope offered by every support group ever formed. Unfortunately most of us fear that we are very much alone, especially in the initial stages of an illness like depression, as we take the first giant step towards getting help. Why have we been singled out and cut off from the rest of the healthy world? Suffering from an illness that many still consider vaguely shameful, we feel set apart from those who are "normal." Tired and despondent, we start to withdraw socially until we really are detached and isolated. Hearing the words "You are not alone" from a doctor, therapist or sympathetic friend with a similar problem can be an enormous relief. The fear of being a social outcast, a freak, a "weirdo," starts to dissolve, and instead we discover our connections to others around us.

When we first meet others who have also been depressed, we are often struck by how *ordinary* everyone looks! One woman describes her experiences in a psychiatrist's waiting room: "At first I was horribly ashamed and embarrassed just to be sitting there; I would hunch down in a chair, nose buried in a book. Then over time I started noticing the other patients coming and going: a woman in a really nice trench coat; a

---

[11]   Theodore Isaac Rubin, M.D., *Compassion and Self-Hate* (New York: Collier Books/ Macmillan Publishing Company, 1986), 223.

friendly young guy in a black leather jacket; an older man with glasses and a briefcase; a teenage boy doing his homework. Lots of patients carried backpacks just like me; maybe they worked downtown too. I knew nothing about them except that we visited the same clinic, but I was comforted by their existence. They didn't look weird! They didn't seem crazy! At church on Sunday when it was time to offer silent prayers of petition, I would think of the other people at the clinic, even though I didn't really know any of them. I realized that we were all in this together."

Experiencing this connection to others who share the same illness is surprisingly comforting; it may be the first step in recognizing our larger connection to each and every person living on this earth. Compared to the vast numbers of humanity, the billions of us covering this huge globe, we tend to restrict ourselves to tiny, closed groups, limited to one family, one neighbourhood, one set of friends, one workplace. We may live in a big city or a small town, but most of the time we ignore the thousands of others who are fellow pilgrims on the long journey of life. Our faith, however, tells us that we are very much connected to these faceless strangers whom we will never know, for every person on this earth has been created in God's image. All human beings have a connection which transcends ethnic, religious, and social boundaries, because all of us have been created by a loving God, the "Father Almighty." Our relationships can have a spiritual dimension, for the good we see in other people reflects God's goodness in creating them.

When struggling with depression, we typically feel isolated from everyone, from family close at home as well as strangers half-way around the world. We need to remind ourselves, over and over again if necessary, that no matter how depression may make us *feel*, we are in fact connected to countless others through our common heritage as God's children. Like the woman who prayed for her fellow patients in the psychiatric clinic, we too can transcend our limited vision to recognize our bond with all the members of this creation.

This world is sometimes a hard and lonely place. Big cities are notoriously impersonal and alienating; small towns are stifling and repressive. A family can be a warm comforting refuge, or a smothering hotbed of resentment. Cynicism is fashionable in certain places; looking down on those outside one's own charmed circle has always been a popular pastime. Look at the value given to the word "exclusive" in advertisements for everything from perfume to real estate! Who wants to be lumped together with a great mass of faceless, boring nobodies?

More constructively, I like to think that I belong to a vast network of talented individuals, most of whom I don't know and never will in this life, but all of whom have something to teach me. The beggar living on the sidewalk, the scientist working on a brilliant discovery, the cashier standing in a supermarket, the farmer ploughing a field with a team of oxen: these four plus the billions of others who walk the face of this earth with me are part of the one human family, my family, God's family. My similarities to these disparate men and women are far greater than my differences. I can think about the lives of all these strangers: look at their faces on the subway, walk with them through the streets of my city, believe that we share common dreams and desires. I can pray for all of us linked by our common humanity. I can trust that I am not alone.

18. Looking Backwards, Looking Sideways

One of the greatest gifts bestowed on our common humanity is that of memory. Because of the wondrous ability to remember, the events of the past are not lost in some black hole of forgetfulness. Like a vast library of personal video tapes detailing my unique life history, my memory holds thousands of ideas, feelings, skills, images and beliefs, and I can replay these tapes whenever I choose. At one time I need to remember "How to Make Caesar Salad." On another day I revisit "The Cottage We Used to Own on Lake Simcoe." The memory of all these past activities, thoughts and experiences profoundly influences the person I am today.

Memory can be very useful in coping with any illness, mental and physical alike. It can be a source of hope as we remember how we have coped with previous episodes of pain and discouragement; it can give comfort as we recall other problems that eventually found solutions; it can strengthen our patience and fortitude as we see how much we have already survived! Unfortunately, depression usually leads us to recall the past in the most bleakly negative way: we dwell on disappointments and castigate ourselves for old mistakes, wasting precious energy on regrets that stretch back to childhood. Our negative memories may be genuine recollections of authentic experiences — here, after all, is proof positive that we really did survive the tortures of adolescence! Nevertheless, we need to be reminded that we can *choose* how we remember. I am the chief operator in the Video Control Booth of my mind; I am entitled to say "enough" if "Making a Mess of My Piano Examination" has been running for three days in a row. In fact, when coping with depression we should be encouraged to remember every past achievement and accomplishment, no matter how silly or insignificant. This is the time to resurrect those old memories that celebrate "How I Cycled 60 Miles in the Pouring Rain at Summer Camp" and "Winning the Spelling Contest in Grade VII." Recalling these old triumphs, *looking backwards* at the events of my past life, I am better prepared to cope with the problems of today.

Then there is *looking sideways* at the experiences of others. We can learn much from one another and from history. A thousand years ago an unknown poet offered comfort and consolation to those suffering from hard times in the Dark Ages; in one of his poems he recounted the trials and tribulations endured and survived by famous heroes and heroines of the mythical past. Each verse, a little tribute to perseverance and strength, ended with this poignant refrain: "Those terrible struggles eventually came to an end; so may today's troubles pass."[12]

We aren't limited to ancient poetry in our search for comfort and consolation, of course; stories of courage in the face of hardship and suffering are everywhere — in the pages of a book, in the personal experiences of our friends, in the articles we read in the newspaper. Remember the story of Margaret and Donald in Chapter 14? When his friends gathered to pay tribute to Donald some weeks after his funeral, they were surprised but greatly comforted by an album of photos that Margaret had made for the occasion. How did she have the courage to look at these pictures which represented her many happy years with Donald? Margaret found the strength because she wanted everyone to remember her wonderful husband and the good times they had shared. This triumph of the human spirit in the midst of terrible grief was an inspiration to all.

---

[12] From "Deor," an Anglo-Saxon poem. The literal translation of the refrain is, "That has passed over; so may this."

When we look sideways at the world around us, we are not setting ourselves up to pass judgment on either the failures or successes we see there; likewise, looking sideways doesn't mean trying to measure up to someone else's standard of behaviour. Rather, looking sideways allows us to see that others struggle just as we do; it helps us to remember that we are not alone; it reinforces the connections that exist between all of us as members of God's family. Best of all, it reminds us that there is always hope. As the poet suggested so many centuries ago, "Others have been able to survive; perhaps I can too."

19. The Courage to Come Back

The Clarke Institute of Psychiatry in Toronto began a programme in 1993 to honour those who had recovered from mental illnesses, physical injuries, chemical dependencies and serious medical conditions. "The Courage to Come Back" campaign recognizes the special men and women whose strength and determination have enabled them to change, adapt, survive and, ultimately, to flourish in the face of severe problems.[13]

Coming back to life after a serious depression is a remarkable experience. The grass looks greener, food tastes better, music sounds beautiful once again; a sense of purpose and pleasure returns to all aspects of human existence. But coming back is a long and sometimes difficult process. I have already mentioned some of the hurdles that most of us face when tackling depression head on: the initial reluctance to get help, the challenges of therapy, the side-effects of medication. As the Clarke Institute acknowledges, it takes courage to climb out of a pit of despair, as well as hard work, patience and humility.

Sometimes when we begin to feel better, "more like ourselves" as we say, we are confronted by yet another obstacle on the already long road to recovery — the need to accept what our depression has meant to others. Very few of us are able to preserve our privacy completely, especially during illness; unless we have been living in a remote cave somewhere,

---

[13] For further details on the "Courage To Come Back" campaign, contact The Clarke Institute of Psychiatry Foundation, 250 College Street, Toronto, Ontario M5T 1R8, (416) 979-6909. The Clarke has purchased the franchise for this campaign from the St. Francis Health Foundation in Pittsburgh, Ohio.

our family, friends, co-workers and neighbours usually suspect that something has been wrong with us. Coming back to life thus includes facing up to a history of uncomfortable moments that others may also have witnessed. As the Clarke recognizes, it takes courage to accept the human limitations associated with illness, the human limitations that we have exposed to the outside world.

One survivor recalls the violent arguments he had with his in-laws about his drinking problem; another feels a twinge of shame every time she remembers her many absences from work, sympathetic though her colleagues were at the time. One survivor carries the memory of a terrible family fight, sure that the neighbours must have heard everything! Yet another regrets the stack of unopened mail, the unpaid bills, the unread letters. One normally polite soul remembers with horror arriving at a party in an obnoxious frame of mind. Doctors and therapists see floods of tears behind the safety of their closed office doors; months later their patients can't forget that someone watched and listened as they cried. Feelings of worthlessness are often part of depression. These feelings can be reinforced if we are ashamed to admit that sometimes we have indeed been tearful, angry, rude, despondent or withdrawn, all the symptoms of depression. We cannot expect to recover until we have the courage to accept ourselves, regardless of what we have done or how we have felt.

There will always be those who laugh at illnesses like depression, who say that the symptoms are imaginary, a sign of weakness or a bid for attention. In their ignorance they will make fun of the process of therapy, the value of medication, the need for time to recover. Given the existence of these sceptics and the stigma still associated with mental illness, it takes courage to admit this truth: "I am less than perfect, indeed so vulnerable and despondent that I have needed professional care to regain my sense of balance and perspective." Perhaps the hardest thing that some of us ever do is to ask for help, yet somewhere we find the courage and strength to do just that.

The courage to come back also includes forgiving others. The roots of problems like depression sometimes lie deep within the sadness of childhood traumas, parental neglect, abuse of every kind. Accepting ourselves as we are, sometimes tearful, angry, rude, despondent or withdrawn, helps us to recognize that those who have hurt us are ordinary human beings who make mistakes too. Yes, parents can be sadistic, spouses can be cruel, children can be inconsiderate. Sometimes friends are disloyal, employers unfair, business competitors ruthless. Every human being who has ever lived has faced temptation, and many, many times we stumble and fall on our journey through life. Yet God can and will forgive us when we ask for pardon, a forgiveness that includes real consolation and healing. The knowledge that we can find forgiveness can in turn inspire us to forgive those who may have contributed to our sorrow and suffering. Without this forgiveness, we cannot be truly whole or healthy.

Human beings are blessed with the ability to grow, to change, to adapt and thus to survive. And to recover from an illness like depression, one that saps the very will to live, we need a multitude of blessings: patience, fortitude, wisdom, humility, and even a sense of humour. We need honesty, too. Some of us are not able to take the first giant steps so important in the process of recovery; not everyone will find the right medication, an effective treatment, a supportive doctor or therapist. Some of us will be lost along the way, and for these we mourn and pray. The journey to recovery has many moments of grace and renewal, and other moments of frustration and disappointment. Only a few survivors will win the official award from the Clarke for bravery and perseverance. But each of us, whenever we recognize God's love, forgiveness and healing, has taken an important step in returning to health and happiness. Honoured and cherished by our Creator, we can honour and cherish ourselves for having the courage to come back.

20. Hope

Researchers recently have emphasized the role of optimism in fighting disease, combatting depression and generally improving the quality of life in an imperfect world. From a spiritual perspective, we speak of *hope* — the trust that we have in God's promise to deliver us from evil, today and tomorrow. Hope looks towards the future with faith in a loving Creator; in this way, the three cardinal virtues of faith, hope and love are inter-related. Hope is not merely a "positive, optimistic attitude," but a response to what we have experienced of God's goodness. Hope has its roots firmly planted in the earth; it pre-supposes a life with challenges, disappointment and illness. When the kingdom of God finally comes to completion and everything in creation has been renewed, we will no longer need hope. But in the meantime, it is crucially important for everyone in this troubled world.

Hope, the sometimes neglected virtue, can help us cope with many aspects of depression. First of all, hope recognizes that depression, like every illness, is a *finite* problem with a finite solution. My faith tells me that every earthly trouble will eventually pass away, sickness and suffering included. However terrible I may feel today, depression is a limited illness of the human brain and mind which cannot destroy all that is good and valuable in myself or in anyone else.

Secondly, hope teaches me to be *realistic* in approaching treatment, while recognizing that I can do something to make a difference to my condition. If I am disappointed by one therapist or medication, hope inspires me to keep looking for another. Remember the old-fashioned proverb, "God helps those who help themselves"? For those suffering from depression, feeling weak and hopeless, it is more reassuring to recognize that God will help me help myself. As we will see in Part IV of this book, fitness, nutrition and relaxation are crucially important self-help tools for those coping with depression.

In the third place, I can rejoice in hope because I am *connected* to others in God's family; I am not alone in my experience of depression. As we have seen elsewhere in this book, I can be sustained in my recovery by the example of others who have survived. In hope, too, I can trust that my loving Creator will support me during my darkest hours.

Fourthly, hope-filled patients are rightly *optimistic*, believing that illnesses can and do change for the better. We recognize that others have indeed recovered; we know the statistics — eighty percent of those with depression can be treated successfully — and we believe this good news! And if our depression does not respond to treatment immediately, hope encourages us to be open to God's future plans for us, whatever they happen to be, while believing that what God intends for us is finally good.

And lastly, in hope, I remain *involved* in the process of my own recovery: committed to learning whatever I can about my problems; keeping my therapy appointments faithfully; following my doctor's instructions about my treatments; taking the best possible care of myself in every way.

The nature of depression, linked as it is to despair and discouragement, leads many of us to imagine that nothing will ever improve; this feeling of hopelessness is in fact a significant symptom of this disease. My belief in God's loving presence can open me up to a new experience of hope, in order to overcome even chronic frustration and pessimism. Through hope, I don't allow myself to be overwhelmed by obsessive thoughts of my illness, nor do I fear that my problems are too big for a solution. In our most negative moments, we feel abandoned by everyone, God included; then we need to remember God's faithfulness and the signs of divine love that we see in others. Hope reminds us that it is only an illusion that no one really cares. In hopelessness, we frequently take refuge behind a mask of indifference, coping with disappointment by claiming that we no longer expect to be well again; through hope, I have the courage to risk, to dare, to plan, and to recover.

We hear so often about the value of strengthening our faith through prayer, spiritual reading, acts of charity, or worship in our community. How do we become hopeful people? While recognizing that hope is more than the power of positive thinking, let me tell you a story that illustrates the way the human mind operates. Imagine this scene: my friend Betty tells me some good news. Her son has finally landed a part-time job to pay for his university tuition; he'll be working as a courier for People's Express. Betty is enormously excited but feels a little deflated when I confess that I've never heard of People's Express. A little miffed by my ignorance, she describes their blue and white trucks; I swear I've never seen even one of them. The next day I go to work as usual and spot five of the People's Express trucks! What happened?[14]

The human mind is bombarded by thousands of pieces of information daily; in any twenty-year period, each person has an average of one

---

[14]   With thanks to psychologist Dr. Bobbe Sommer who used this example at her workshop, "Negativity in the Workplace," on April 5, 1995, Toronto, Ontario.

billion experiences![15] To keep from being overwhelmed, the mind unconsciously filters out much of what we see, hear, feel, and so on. But once we are alerted to the significance of something — like the People's Express trucks — the filtering process changes. Now the mind starts looking specifically for the highlighted item; that's why I noticed the trucks after my conversation with Betty. This highly useful aspect of the mind/brain connection can help us "tune in to hope." By consciously looking for things that lift our spirits when we feel hopeless, we acquire valuable ammunition in the ongoing battle against despair and inertia.[16]

How can we re-set our minds to notice all the reasons for hope in this world? Some swear by the positive effects of fitness, meditation or relaxation exercises. One woman goes to a park and watches children at play; she says, "Here are the doctors, scientists and teachers of tomorrow. Their happiness and joy for life gives me hope." We can look for inspiration in the words of others, through the pages of Scripture, in great literature, even in the lyrics of a popular song. One teenager quotes these hopeful lines: "Standing on a hill on a mountain of dreams / Telling myself it's not as hard, as hard, as hard as it seems."[17] We can look to the example of others who have shown hope in action; I am motivated by the history of the cathedral-builders of the Middle Ages, men and women who worked with devotion and skill on enormous, almost overwhelming projects, while knowing that they might never see the finished results. Another person may be encouraged by the perseverance and fortitude of the early Canadian pioneers and homesteaders. One man says he finds his inspiration closer to home, remembering the dedication and patience of his mother, a widow who raised four sons alone.

---

[15]   Tom Miller, Ph.D., "Self-discipline and Emotional Control: How To Stay Calm and Productive under Pressure," Seminar workbook available with audiocassette (Boulder, CO.: CareerTrack Publications, 1992), 12A. This is one example of a workbook used in cognitive therapy (see Chapter 30).

[16]   As St. Paul says in Philippians 4:8: "Whatever is true, whatever is honourable, whatever is just, whatever is pure, whatever is pleasing, whatever is commendable, if there is any excellence and if there is anything worthy of praise, think about these things."

[17]   Led Zeppelin, "Goin' to California," from *Led Zeppelin,* Warner Electra Atlantic, CD-82638, 1971.

It takes faith to have hope in this trying world. The words of Psalm 23 are perhaps the most famous, most quoted verses in the whole Bible. Here is God's promise to me, no matter what may come in my life:

> Even though I walk through the darkest valley,
> I fear no evil, for you are with me;
> your rod and your staff — they comfort me.

21. Balance

This book uses the image of sunshine and shadow to explore some of the facets of depression, as well as the links between spirituality and illness. The contrast between these two natural conditions reminds us that a healthy life includes balance — the balance between rest and activity, work and recreation, sad and happy moods. Understanding the function of sadness in the balance of a happy life is a challenge, if we mistakenly believe that healthy people should be cheerful all the time. Experience teaches another lesson.

In the 1970s I enjoyed several wonderful vacations in Baja California, Mexico, camping on remote beaches under cloudless, brilliantly blue skies. Those of us visiting from the frozen North loved the hot, dry weather guaranteed to last all winter long. Unfortunately, the lack of rain that we enjoyed so much was a mixed blessing; this part of the peninsula had been suffering for many years from an extended drought that seriously affected local agriculture. Tourists forget that without a little regular precipitation it is impossible to grow anything! We cannot live our whole lives in conditions of unremitting sunshine; we need rain to wash us clean, fresh air to blow away the cobwebs after sleep, cool breezes to calm us after a long hot spell of anger. We say that a summer thunderstorm "clears the air"; this is an appropriate metaphor for some of life's more dramatic confrontations. Human existence consists of challenge, variety and change, in short, days of sunshine alternating with days of shadow.

No one can reasonably expect a lifetime of cloudless blue skies, when every morning feels like the first day of summer holidays. Depression might be described as a never-ending November of endless drizzle and grey; on the other hand, recovery does not mean a future without storm clouds, those problems of life everyone has to face. When our depression lifts we may experience an initial excitement and rejuvenation, like those first wonderful spring days when everything feels green and alive again. Such euphoria may lead to unreasonable expectations for the future: "I don't ever have to feel down again," or, "I won't be able to cope if the depression comes back." One brave survivor, describing the common misconceptions about anti-depressant medication, singled out friends who said, "I thought your pills were supposed to make you feel good all the time."[18] Depression is not always like a broken leg that heals once and for all; our problems may very well require on-going maintenance, long-term medication and continuing self-discipline. Although eighty percent of those suffering from depression can be helped, researchers are still looking for medications that will benefit the other twenty percent who cannot be treated successfully at this time. Some of us with serious relapses have to start the whole process of treatment all over again. Recovery from depression doesn't mean freedom from all illness forevermore; human beings are vulnerable to disease and accident, and each one of us will eventually die.

Instead of looking for eternally cloudless skies in this life, we will have a more fruitful and satisfying time if we aim to establish a balance in our expectations: to accept the sunshine and shadow that belong to the human condition; to work at an ongoing, *lifelong* recovery while enjoying as much as possible the joys of everyday living. Those of us who have experienced dramatic mood swings, from the very high peaks of energy and excitement to the very deep valleys of discouragement and fatigue, can learn ways to cope with these extremes. With appropriate care, the valleys are not as deep as they used to be. We find new and more reliable ways to climb out of the pit of despair, trusting our instincts more and more, even while praying sincerely for God's help in staying well.

The following lines of Scripture have been quoted time and time again to illustrate the need for balance in a healthy life. Depression is an illness that prevents us from coping with the regular rhythms of human life, the

---

[18] Kathy Cronkite, *On the Edge of Darkness: Conversations about Conquering Depression* (New York: Doubleday, 1994), 190.

ups and downs alike. In this discussion of sunshine and shadow together, it is helpful to remember these comforting words:

For everything there is a season,
and a time for every matter under heaven:

. . .

a time to weep, and a time to laugh; a time to mourn,
and a time to dance.[19]

As the writer of these words said, God has made a time for everything, including the experience of sadness. We who have seen what it means to weep as well as to laugh have learned a valuable lesson about the nature of life's journey.

22. Thanksgiving

Over a lifetime we receive countless presents from the God of surprises; the process of unwrapping the gift of illness can be an important part of our life's journey, especially if we take a positive approach to this challenge. While learning to understand and accept the mysterious and providential events of every lifetime, ultimately we need and want to say "thank you" for the precious gift of life itself. Saying "thank you" to God can open us up to the great power of prayer.

Prayer is the only way I can communicate with my Creator. As an expression of our relationship, it reflects me as I am: a unique individual who sometimes feels happy, sad, frustrated, satisfied, angry, serene, afraid, or triumphant. As a complete human being — body, soul, mind and strength — I pray with everything that is human — my thoughts and feelings, words and actions; with song, dance, gesture; tears and laughter, imagination and spontaneity. Furthermore, my prayers of thanksgiving can reflect my gratitude for everything: the happy, sad, frustrating, satisfying, angry, serene, fearful and triumphant moments that, added together, make one human life.

---

[19]   Ecclesiastes 3:1, 4.

Prayer has been called "an attitude of gratitude."[20] Our attitudes shape and influence our thoughts, activities and feelings, day after day, consciously and unconsciously; an attitude of gratitude can turn every event into a potentially enriching experience, not just those that are conventionally regarded as positive and helpful. Throughout this book I have taken an "attitude of gratitude" for the good things that can come out of illness, and especially out of depression, but do not assume that such a perspective is always easy to maintain. Sometimes it is an enormous struggle to preserve a positive outlook, especially when the sunshine disappears and everything is bleak and colourless in the shadow. Nevertheless, we need to remember, especially in our darkest moments, that God knows and cares about everything that happens to this world and to each of us. This simple fact forms the basis for our gratitude; this truth can sustain us through all of life's experiences. Perhaps we cannot give thanks *for* everything, but as St. Paul advises in one of his letters, we can give thanks *in* all circumstances.[21]

Appreciating everything that comes our way is often a profoundly difficult challenge; saying "thank you" requires us to admit that suffering is sometimes a puzzling, challenging mystery. As I learned from watching my friend Margaret cope with the grim reality of her husband's death while she was pregnant with their first child, it is insulting and ultimately futile to pretend that prayer and faith will make everything "all right." Rather, it makes more sense to say that prayer and our faith help us to cope when things most definitely are not "all right."

The tragedies of life, including illness and bereavement, often help us to focus on the simple gifts that answer our most basic human needs — food and drink for hunger and thirst, warmth on a cold night, light in the darkness. Suffering of any kind can sharpen our appreciation of these necessities, because when all is going well we rarely remember to say "thank you" for the bed we sleep in and the water that we drink. Our prayers of thanksgiving come naturally at life's special moments, the weddings and baptisms and graduations. How often do we remember to express the same gratitude while washing the dinner dishes? There are

---

[20] With thanks to Roger Bonneau, O. Carm.

[21] 1 Thessalonians 5:18.

many reasons to feel thankful while performing this humble activity: the very existence of food and china at a time when many are homeless and hungry; the abundance of clean water and cheap soap, resources often taken for granted in a developed country; the ability to stand and work when others are too weak even to sit and eat. Human beings throughout the ages have composed odes, masses, canticles, and hymns to celebrate the great public triumphs of the day. Too often we ignore the *simple* gifts, like having the strength and energy to wash the dinner dishes. Does it seem eccentric to suggest that we compose our own private Dish Washing Prayers of Thanksgiving? An illness like depression teaches us that even these humble activities should be greeted with thanksgiving and joy.

By focusing on the meaning of every moment of life, the trivial and the profound, the sublime and the ridiculous alike, prayers of thanksgiving help me to give "today" the attention that it deserves. Regrets for the past and worries for the future become less distracting if I am living here in the present and valuing each moment as it passes. A reminder: I can't *enjoy* each and every minute of my life. Pain remains pain, scrapes and bruises still hurt, lost car keys are still a nuisance. I don't ask myself to smile at a time when tears are the appropriate emotional response. I know that it is not *easy* to be grateful, patient and accepting during times of great stress or suffering. But in my heart I try to feel a little gratitude, no matter what is happening around me, through the simple belief that every gift in life, sunshine and shadow, sorrow and celebration, has a purpose in God's sometimes mysterious plan for this world. For this I am learning to say "thank you" to my loving Creator.

Part III

Hiding under the Shadow

. . . a spiritual journey into the shadow of depression . . .

> Anger
> Guilt and shame
> Self-hate
> Suicide
> Poisons
> Neglect
> Inertia
> Doubt
> Fatigue
> Agitation
> Sadness

23. Anger

There's an old story about a famous poet who was asked to contribute an essay on pride to a book about the Seven Deadly Sins. The editors were dismayed when they received the manuscript which began, "Pride has always been one of my favourite virtues." The famous poet had blurred the distinction between an over-inflated ego and the justified appreciation of one's true worth. Some of the same ambivalence surrounds anger, an emotion that is considered sinful and destructive on the one hand, and normal and even therapeutic on the other.

Many of us fear anger because of negative childhood experiences, running away from anything that reminds us of our parents' or teachers' outbursts. One man commented on his early life: "My father was an alcoholic who yelled and screamed at us constantly. Even when Dad wasn't drinking, his terrible temper didn't really improve. He was addicted to rage too." Today, this man reacts to the memory of his father's anger by going to the opposite extreme; he is often drawn into friendships with those who are meek, self-effacing, non-aggressive. He copes with anger by pretending that it shouldn't exist.

The denial of anger does a great disservice to our nature as complex creatures who experience a rainbow of different feelings and moods. Every one of our emotions is part of our unique human heritage; we cannot decide that some of these emotions are good, while condemning other emotions as bad. We are not responsible for our emotions — only for how we act upon them. Anger, along with other so-called negative emotions like envy or fear, does not disappear merely because we declare that good people shouldn't feel this way. Rather, repressing these thoughts and feelings often causes them to be expressed in more destructive ways.

Repressed anger can be as dangerous as uncontrolled rage. In the shadow of depression there often lurk years of resentment, hatred, bitterness and irritation, all pushed underground and left to fester; such repression can cause all our emotions to be blanketed in a thick fog. If we are not allowed to feel everything that we are as complete human beings, including these less-than-desirable emotions such as anger, we sometimes lose the ability to feel anything at all.

Women are especially ambivalent towards emotions which are labelled "dangerous" by society; we fear that the normal expression of anger will turn us into ugly caricatures — the nagging wife, the bitter spinster, the bossy mother-in-law. Many of us were taught that ladies are supposed to be cool and calm, a dramatic contrast to the entirely warm-blooded and emotionally healthy expression of anger. Too often we fear that being angry means losing control; if we really let go, a lifetime's accumulation of ugly words might spill out, causing irreparable damage to ourselves, threatening relationships, frightening our families, destroying the carefully contrived mask of calmly ordered logic that rational people are supposed to wear.

Everyone has good reasons to feel anger at one time or another. Whole books have been written on this universal human experience.[1] At times this world is a cruel and unjust place, with enough examples of incompetence and injustice to inspire outrage in the most temperate, yet

---

[1] Besides *Compassion and Self-Hate,* mentioned above in Chapter 16, Theodore Isaac Rubin has written *The Angry Book* (New York: Collier Books, Macmillan Publishing Company, 1969). This small handbook sold over 800,000 copies! There is obviously a great demand for information on our negative emotions.

we fear even this righteous anger. Think of that common expression: "the patience of a saint." Associating the absence of anger with the presence of virtue causes many of us to misunderstand this much maligned emotion. Perhaps we can change our perspective by remembering all the scriptural examples of anger: Yahweh infuriated by human folly and calling down the destruction of the great flood; Moses descending from Mount Sinai to destroy the golden calf, smashing the tablets of the ten commandments in the process; Jesus driving the money-changers from the temple with furious energy. Neatness and order, control and logic are sometimes less important than well-expressed anger; in some situations plain words and raised voices are the most appropriate responses.

While some may fear anger, there are others among us who are not at all timid about expressing this emotion. Do your family and friends hear too many plain words and raised voices? If this is the situation in your life, perhaps now is the time to look at the meaning and emotion behind those constantly angry words. Many of us have much in our hearts that needs to be reconciled; we carry a burden prepared years before and never lifted, a weight of hostility and resentment created by ill-treatment and unfairness from long ago. We seethe about life's injustices, major and minor, and the anger inspired by yesterday's grievances spills over, poisoning today's relationships. Left-over anger sours our ability to enjoy life; unresolved frustration from the past prevents us from accepting the goodness that belongs to the present.

Anger is part of the shadow of all human life, including the shadow of depression. Part of life's journey includes learning more about ourselves and all our emotions, including the sources of our anger and the ways we have expressed *or* repressed this normal human response in the past. We need to listen to ourselves, paying attention to the roots of our feelings. Do you hear disappointment, fear, sadness, frustration inside your anger? Opening our hearts and souls to the meaning of all our emotions can help us to accept the existence of and the need for healthy, human anger.

24. Guilt and Shame

"God, forgive me." This simple prayer is sometimes built upon an enormously complex distortion, one that leads far away from true reconciliation into a sea of self-hatred and fear. During the experience of depression, many of us believe that we are worthless, sinful failures adrift on the vast ocean of a wasted life. We search for comfort, understanding, acceptance; we spend hours on a fruitless quest for healing, never recognizing the origin of our cry for forgiveness. Exploring the feelings of depression can reveal a sad hiding place deep within the human soul: the place where we feel guilt and shame.

Guilt is often confused with shame, but although these two feed on each other, they are somewhat different in nature. I feel guilty because of something I have done; my conscience bothers me and I may experience remorse and regret. The guilt may be justified or not, but it always follows some actual event — neglecting a responsibility, forgetting a promise, ignoring a plea for help. Shame, however, is a flood of negative feelings inspired by contempt for who I am; it is also associated with the fear that others too will see me as a "bad person." As we saw in Chapter 2, "excessive or inappropriate guilt" is an important symptom of depression, so it is always necessary first to distinguish between true and false guilt. Each of us is a fallible human creature who makes mistakes and needs forgiveness, from God and from others. At the same time we can confuse the need for pardon and reconciliation belonging to "true guilt" with the unquenchable feelings of "unforgivable shame" that are part of the experience of depression.

All the great religions have attempted to govern human behaviour through moral teachings and philosophies. But when we are depressed, vulnerable to *inappropriate* feelings of *excessive* guilt and shame, we don't limit ourselves to commandments. The rules for ordered conduct are only the beginning! Instead, we let our imaginations run wild, finding more and more to criticize and condemn, until we despise virtually everything in our lives. Hence the futility of our prayers for reconciliation, our desperate attempts to believe that God really pardons our failings. Unfortunately God's acceptance is not enough for us; through the nature of our illness, we are unable to accept ourselves.

Those of us who know excessive guilt and shame through depression have somehow become overly sensitive to our human limitations. As a result, we are ashamed of so much: our hunger for food, our desire for sexual expression, our yearning for approval, our need for human warmth.

Our memories retain the guilty images of past mistakes that still trouble us in the present, while conveniently forgetting our good deeds, acts of charity and positive triumphs of virtue, past and present. Often in the process of healing depression, through therapy for example, we learn more about reconciling our inevitable human failures with our potential for goodness. As we saw above in Chapter 15, humility means accepting strengths and weaknesses honestly, recognizing what is a strength and what is a weakness, what is fact and what is delusion. Until we can cope with the reality of our moral strengths and weaknesses, reconciling our lapses to the ideals set before us, we will be forever trapped on a treadmill of self-justification. We will never be content with what we have, who we are, what we do. However we understand the meaning of God's expectations of humanity, does God expect perfection?

Furthermore, guilt and shame are sometimes twisted into a distortion of pride that takes the place of healthy self-esteem. Wrapping our consciences in a cloak of false humility, we stand aloof from the rest of the world, as if we were the only suffering sinners on this earth. Like naughty children, we say, "Look at me: I'm special because I'm bad." How much spiritual energy is wasted in maintaining this shell of humiliation and alienation! Meanwhile, locked into the habit of focusing on non-existent failings and mistakes from long ago, we miss the opportunity to be a true child of God, changing and growing today, receiving God's peace and knowing God's love right now.

Robert Karen, in an article on "Shame" in *The Atlantic Monthly* (February 1992), states that "the concept of shame had until recently all but vanished from discussions of emotional disarray. Now it is regarded by many psychologists as the pre-eminent cause of emotional distress in our time." Systematically unravelling the knot of guilt and shame that strangles our freedom to love and laugh may be a difficult process, requiring prayer and meditation, much compassion and patience, perhaps even professional help. Rarely have we become prisoners of our own self-hatred overnight; it takes years of practice, usually starting in childhood, aided and abetted by the lifelong *perception* of failure. We might begin by meditating on the fact of God's love for us as we really are, sunshine and shadow alike. Have we established an unrealistic ideal of cool, detached perfection, an ideal that none of us ever achieves? Are we suspicious of our emotions, the very heart and soul of human life, the rush of thoughts and feelings that add colour and light to every moment of existence? Have we twisted the need for control and order — the rules and regulations and commandments — into the systematic repression of emotion and desire? Do we have two sets of rules: one rigid and strict for ourselves, one charitably lenient for others? When did we become so afraid of what we are? Does God really want us to live like machines?

"God, forgive me" is an appropriate prayer for the times when I am envious, judgmental and lazy, and can acknowledge these failings with honesty and humility. But I was not meant to be a sterile, lifeless object that never makes mistakes and never feels embarrassment, never loves or grows or lives. I pray for the wisdom to accept myself as a human being, and the compassion to love myself as God loves me: exactly as I am.

25. Self-Hate

The first chapter of this book ends with a scriptural quotation, the first part of the great commandment which Jesus gives his followers: "You shall love the Lord your God with all your heart, and with all your soul, and with all your mind, and with all your strength." These powerful words ask for a serious commitment: our relationship to our loving Creator is meant to involve every facet of our being, including imagination, intelligence, creativity, humour and physical grace. But Jesus has more to say about love. After asking us to give our whole selves to God, he continues with the second part of the command: "You shall love your neighbour as yourself."[2]

Jesus is making an assumption when he says that we should love our neighbours as we love ourselves. What about those who hate themselves? Many people in the depths of depression neglect the simplest daily necessities — appropriate food, rest, hygiene. They may blame themselves for a host of errors and omissions, past and present. Jesus does not command us to love ourselves; he assumes that healthy people take care of their own interests first and need to be reminded to think of

---

[2]   Mark 12:28-34.

others, too. Those who suffer from depression also need a gentle reminder, a warning that the very nature of their disease creates an overwhelming alienation within, preventing them from acknowledging and satisfying their own needs and desires. Many of us with depression will struggle to take care of others; out of sheer willpower we might be able to feed our families or go to work, but then we stop. We might accept the command to love God and our neighbours, but we don't know very much about loving ourselves.

Self-hatred, on the other hand, flourishes everywhere. It can take many forms, from the most blatantly destructive violence to the subtle sabotage that slowly but inexorably chips away at self-esteem. Consistently taking on projects that require unrealistic commitments of time and energy; choosing harmful relationships that cause repeated sorrow and disappointment; finding endless excuses to neglect health, fitness, nutrition — these are some examples of destructive self-hatred in action. A few of us make boldly dramatic gestures like suicide; we can do almost as much damage indirectly, as though we have forgotten what it means to love ourselves.

How do we hate ourselves? Let us count the ways. John, a social worker, feels inadequate compared to his best friend who is a prominent lawyer. Although he is successful in his field, John doesn't make as much money as his friend, and therefore in his own eyes he is a failure. Larry, a well-known criminal lawyer, is constantly worried about his investments and frustrated by having to defend various shady characters in his law practice. He regrets that he didn't spend his life in a more satisfying career, perhaps as a social worker or teacher. Colleen is a single woman who is ashamed that she has never married. In spite of a healthy income and an interesting career, she refuses to make a home for herself. Buying a house is a reward she denies herself because she has never found a husband. Catherine, a woman with a very demanding family life, feels guilty because her unmarried friends are more involved with their volunteer work than she can be. Struggling to keep up, she refuses to accept that she has less time, energy and money than the others. These real-life examples[3] show only a few of the subtle ways in which we deny our unique needs

---

[3]   Names and some details have been changed.

and wants, hating who we really are, thinking we should be more like someone else.

The mass media — television, magazines, newspapers — are full of helpful hints on ways we can improve our lives, fuelling the relentless struggle to be better, to do more, to climb higher. How can we take time to care for ourselves when there is still so much to do: try another interesting recipe; learn another state-of-the-art computer system; read another inspiring book; visit another important art exhibition? Will we ever be finished the life-long quest for perfection, the endless process of turning ourselves into someone worthy of our own love and respect? This is the silent, subtle self-hatred that many of us feel: we cannot accept ourselves as we are today. Tomorrow perhaps, after we have lost a little more weight or completed one more course or added a few more thousands to our bank account. Then we might be good enough to merit our own esteem.

Learning to love ourselves is a lifelong challenge, especially when confronted by the negative emotions associated with depression: anger, self-hatred, shame and guilt. Furthermore, depression is not a simple problem with a simple solution; it is an insult to our complexity as unique individuals to suggest that there is one easy answer. We began this chapter by remembering that we have been commanded to love God and our neighbour. It is also valuable to remember that we respond to God's love in many different ways through the course of one human life. Yes, it is important to acknowledge the needs of those around us, the "neighbours" whom we are commanded to love. But I believe that whenever I am good to myself — making time for rest, talking about my problems to a trusted friend, working less to enjoy my life more — I am also doing something valuable and holy. I am treating one of God's creatures with love.[4]

---

[4]   St. Thomas Aquinas taught that our Creator has implanted in every creature the inclination to love itself, to conserve itself in existence, and to resist forces that would destroy it.

26. Suicide

Please note: the following information on suicide prevention is aimed specifically at those whose depression is troubled by frequent morbid thoughts of death or dying. For those tempted to consider suicide because of chronic physical pain or terminal illness, please contact a hospital or hospice that provides appropriate palliative care and counselling.

The ultimate expression of self-hatred is suicide, both a public and private statement of despair and self-loathing. In ages past, suicide was seen as an affront to ordered, integrated society for many reasons. It was treated as a crime because it weakened the collective strength of the state; it was considered a sin, forbidden by the commandment, "Thou shalt not kill." The body of the victim could not find rest in consecrated ground but was banished to ignominious burial at a crossroads, a lost, lonely place outside the boundaries of the community.

Even today, when we have far greater understanding of the workings of the human mind, those pushed to this final extreme are sometimes condemned as selfish because their actions hurt so many others. Often the family and friends of the victim are left to wonder, "What else could we have done?" and to struggle with their own burden of anger and guilt. At the same time, experts recognize suicidal intentions as a symptom of serious mental illness (such as severe depression or schizophrenia) or the result of painful, tortured desperation. Such sympathy does not minimize the public and private tragedy of extreme self-hatred; it does not condone, let alone encourage, any attack on the sanctity of all human life. Instead, those who are moved by compassion seek to understand and then to help, so that anyone who feels desperate can receive appropriate medical treatment.

The human mind is like a huge workroom of thoughts, feelings and memories; it loves to create and imagine. Most of us at one time or another will think about the inevitable: we imagine what it might be like to die. We sometimes write our own obituaries or plan our own funerals, calmly envisioning an event that will surely take place sooner or later. *However, frequent morbid thoughts of death or dying are not healthy!* There is a difference between the rare and fleeting fantasy of creative imagination, and dangerous obsession.

Frequent thoughts about death or the formulation of concrete plans for dying are early warning signals that something inside body or mind is seriously out of balance. If you are troubled in this way, call someone immediately — a pastoral counsellor, family doctor, therapist, close friend or relative. Furthermore, if you confide your thoughts and fears to someone who then brushes your anxieties aside, please do not let your genuine concerns be ignored. Every suicide threat should be taken seriously. Sometimes friends and family respond to talk about suicide with thoughtless remarks such as, "Don't be so silly," or, "It will pass," or, "You're making a mountain out of a molehill." If your first effort to find help is unsuccessful, try again! Remember: suicidal thoughts that stem from depression and other mental illnesses are not signs of a weak will; they are symptoms of a recognizable illness. An experienced doctor or therapist will never dismiss your concerns lightly.

Furthermore, self-destructive acts are not solely the domain of flamboyant Hollywood celebrities looking for attention (though, God knows, even celebrities are entitled to compassion and treatment). Ordinary people are also tortured by self-hatred and desperation. Emily,[5] once a vibrant teenager who loved sports, deteriorated dramatically during a severe depression; an alert guidance counsellor spotted a dangerous obsession and helped her to get appropriate treatment. Pat was plagued by sleepless nights and feelings of despair after an operation; he was deeply ashamed of these feelings because he considered himself to be a person of strong faith. He is thankful today that a concerned and sympathetic doctor listened to his fears, then prescribed an effective medication which relieved his anxiety. His distorted thoughts about death and dying never became a reality. Emily and Pat are real people who lived unremarkable lives not complicated by fame and fortune. Furthermore, from the perspective of faith we look forward to an ultimate union with our Creator after this life, but it is not a sign of piety, virtue or holiness to dwell obsessively on death, dying and destruction. The suicidal thoughts and fantasies which are sometimes a part of depression can and should be treated.

---

[5] Names and some details have been changed.

It is not appropriate to speak of suicide as an unforgivable sin; no one can see into the mind of God nor into the soul of one who has been driven to this tragic act. It is not our business to judge! On the other hand, the growing acceptance of euthanasia, mercy killing or doctor-assisted suicide in our society is a denial of the value of all life, life that is precious not because it is beautiful or worthwhile or rewarding, but because it is a gift from God, a gift whose value cannot be measured in human terms alone.

If you have a friend or relative who talks frequently of suicide or death, don't try to handle this serious problem alone: contact a family doctor, distress centre or professional therapist for advice. If you yourself are troubled by thoughts and feelings about death, do not play with dangerous ideas like these: "Everyone would be much happier without me," or, "I'm tired and just want to be at peace," or, "No one will miss me anyway," or, "Maybe when I'm gone, then they'll be sorry." Call for help immediately.

Sometimes suicide and other self-destructive acts are described as courageous deeds undertaken by strong, starkly realistic heroes. This is nonsense. We have already seen some of the ethical reasons against suicide. Medically speaking, doctors and therapists recognize that the basic instinct of all living creatures is the instinct for self-preservation. Anything that undermines this drive for life and growth is unhealthy, and is usually based on self-hatred and delusional thinking. For this reason, suicidal thoughts are considered to be one of the symptoms of depression.

If you are desperate and don't know where to turn, call "411" (Directory Assistance) or "911" (Emergency) and ask to be connected to a local distress centre. Distress centres are staffed by sympathetic, trained operators who will listen to your concerns and direct you to further help as required. If warranted, the emergency operator will also send police, ambulance services or the fire department.

Likewise, case workers from Children's Aid Societies respond promptly to problems with troubled adolescents. (Call Directory Assistance for the number in your area.) Some teenagers may be fascinated by self-mutilation; often what seems to be a bizarre "fad," influenced by contemporary music and fashion, is actually a desperate cry for help, the sign of an underlying depression and serious self-hatred that needs appropriate medical attention. Speak to your family doctor or a school guidance counsellor for professional advice.

27. Poisons

Please note: this review of the dangers of alcohol, tobacco, caffeine and street drugs is intended to highlight their destructive potential as poisons. It is not meant to criticize or discourage the appropriate use of prescription medication for the treatment of depression or any other medical condition.

Alcohol, tobacco, caffeine: our society tolerates a wide variety of stimulants and mood-altering substances. We call them *drugs*, the same word we use for medicine, because they act in the body in the same way. Drugs of all kinds have been known since the dawn of civilization: prehistoric peoples brewed beer and fermented wine for celebrations, chewed the leaves of plants for strength, smoked special herbs and consumed psychedelic mushrooms for visions. Furthermore, many types of chemicals play a recognized role in today's social customs: we gather for a cup of coffee during a break at work and traditionally raise a glass of champagne at a wedding. Many Christians think it puritanical to condemn the responsible use of alcohol; after all, the first miracle of Jesus' public life involved changing water into wine at the marriage feast in Cana. On the other hand, some of us turn to these mood-altering substances not as part of healthy, social celebrations but in a desperate attempt to cope with feelings of frustration and sadness, anger and loneliness. This is especially true during depression, when our moods cry out to be altered. In fact, studies have shown that one-third of those suffering from depression also experience some form of substance abuse or dependence.[6]

Every culture makes its own rules about certain social customs. Currently in Canada there is public tolerance for alcohol and caffeine; tobacco may be sold legally, but smoking in public places is restricted and

---

[6]   From the fact sheet "Depression: Treat it. Defeat it." United States Department of Health and Human Services — Depression Awareness, Recognition and Treatment Program.

its private use is often criticized; street drugs are officially considered unacceptable and dangerous. The generic term "chemical," however, emphasizes the similarity between all these substances. The motivation behind their use is remarkably consistent. Most of the time we drink (coffee, cola or cognac), smoke, or use drugs in an effort to feel different in some way: more awake, less nervous, more energetic, less inhibited. The use of chemicals in response to the trials and tribulations of illnesses like depression is now called "self-medication." In other words, we are saying, "I want to change how I feel, and to do this I use the familiar drugs that are close at hand in my world." Depending on our cultural or social backgrounds, "familiar drugs" might mean white wine, cigarettes, chocolate bars or sleeping pills. This is not to suggest that because society tolerates alcohol, tobacco and caffeine, other drugs should therefore be permitted. Rather it is a warning that all chemicals are potentially dangerous because society as a whole has developed a tolerance to a variety of "mood-altering substances." We have found many ingenious and sometimes unhealthy ways to escape from the reality of how we feel.

While accepting that the experience of pleasure is part of the attraction behind the use of chemicals, we must also face the fact that the potential for abuse is equally real. Because chemicals can help us feel calm, energetic, relaxed or alert, it is sometimes easier to turn to drugs rather than to sort out our lives so that we feel naturally calm, energetic, relaxed or alert. Look at the way coffee has become the acceptable morning stimulant, the perfect antidote when we feel tired after a night of poor sleep.

Every chemical, including prescription medications, has side-effects; many are well known, such as the increased risk of heart and lung problems from the use of tobacco. Sometimes the side-effects are actually considered desirable: caffeine is such an acceptable stimulant that in some circles it is considered eccentric to refuse a cup of coffee. Alcohol is a powerful depressant; it is *not* a stimulant, as is commonly supposed. The first few drinks may lift our spirits and loosen our inhibitions, but with overuse there comes a long, destructive crash to the bottom. Alcohol in excess also damages liver and brain cells, causes recognizable personality changes, and impairs our ability to think clearly. As for street drugs, these come with a lengthy list of dangers, from the possibility of overdoses and impurities to the very real risk of well-entrenched addiction to illegal and expensive poison. Given these potential dangers, why are chemicals still so popular? Researchers have proposed various conflicting theories to explain the prevalence of abuse and dependency: cultural climate, genetic predisposition, or chemical imbalances. There are an equal number of theories about the *treatment* of abuse and dependency.

Furthermore, chemical dependence, substance abuse and addictive behaviours of all kinds are both symptoms and causes of self-hatred. True happiness and contentment are not usually found at the bottom of a bottle; the after-effect of disgust soon wipes away the memory of enjoyment and relaxation. Given today's knowledge about the dangers of smoking, the continued use of tobacco implies a certain reckless disregard for personal health and safety. Compulsive eating, spending and gambling are likewise related to chronic self-hatred; they may begin as a search for pleasure, but eventually these compulsive activities destroy health — physical, mental and financial. The literature on drug and alcohol abuse abounds in poignant descriptions of degradation and despair. In fact, many of us develop addictions because we want to be punished in some way; while slower and less dramatic than suicide, compulsive behaviour of any kind can turn our lives into a living hell. And we do this to ourselves on purpose! There is also a religious dimension to addiction and dependency. Do we turn to chemicals and addictive behaviours to punish ourselves because we refuse to accept God's forgiveness and healing love? Are we reluctant to surrender our lives into the power of Another? Depression mixed with alcohol or drugs is a particularly lethal combination; the two problems become twisted and intertwined, one feeding upon the other, until very little self-respect, energy and pleasure is left in life.

Because I have seen too many lives scarred by drinking, I have adopted these rules for the responsible use of alcohol:

- *Never drink alone*, especially when feeling depressed, lonely, angry or frustrated.
- *Enjoy one or two drinks* with a meal, but, except on special occasions, skip the pre-dinner cocktails and the after-dinner liqueurs and brandy. Experts differ on the number of drinks which

are safe to consume in one week; I prefer to exercise caution and restrict myself to one glass of wine or beer with dinner.

- At a party that will last for several hours, *begin the evening with a non-alcoholic soft drink or mineral water.* Enjoy one or two alcoholic drinks in the middle of the evening, then return to the mineral water and soft drinks. *Always have something to eat when drinking.*

- *Learn to say No.* The Addiction Research Foundation suggests, "Before going to a social event, you should always plan effective ways of saying 'No' to yourself and 'No' to others."[7] In a perfect world, our friends and relatives would graciously accept our answers without argument whenever we decline anything that is offered to us, food or drink. This is not a perfect world, so until you can say a simple but firm, "No, thanks," think of ways to answer those who insist, in the name of misguided hospitality, that you join them in drinking.

- *Avoid alcohol during the day,* especially if you regularly enjoy wine or liqueurs in the evening.

- *Develop a taste for adult non-alcoholic beverages:* mineral water with lemon or lime, orange juice and soda, tonic and bitters, iced tea, tomato juice with spices ("Virgin Mary" or "Virgin Caesar"), mulled non-alcoholic cider, lemonade, fruit punch, flavoured hot chocolate, or herbal teas. There are more and more healthy and delicious choices available everywhere!

- *Choose drinks with a lower alcohol content* such as light beer or spritzers (wine and soda.) For mixed drinks, ask for extra soda, tonic, ginger ale, cola.

- As a host, *never force anyone else to drink.* Offer alcohol to guests once only; if it is refused, don't push, tease or cajole.

If the above list of suggestions strikes you as silly, be careful. Problem drinkers laugh off the need for guidelines for the responsible use of

---

[7] Martha Sanchez-Craig, *Saying When: How to Quit Drinking or Cut Down* (Toronto, Addiction Research Foundation, 1994), 45. To order this excellent self-help handbook, call the ARF at 1-800-661-1111.

alcohol because they are looking to experience the *effects* of their drinks as quickly as possible. Remember: thirty-two percent of those with depression also have problems with alcohol or drugs.

The Betty Ford Centre for the treatment of drug and alcohol abuse is famous for helping celebrities from around the world; there is even a listing for this high-profile California facility in the Toronto telephone book! Thankfully, there are many resources closer to home for those who are concerned about serious drinking, drug use or addictive/compulsive behaviours:

- *DART (The Drug and Alcohol Registry of Treatment*, 1-800-565-8603) is an agency that offers referrals to OHIP-covered treatment facilities in local communities. Counsellors direct callers to assessment and referral services for a preliminary consultation. In Toronto there is the *Metro Addiction Assessment and Referral Service*, (416) 481-1446. *DART* is limited to residents of Ontario, but similar services are available elsewhere. In Quebec, call *Drug Health Referral*, 1-800-265-2626. In British Columbia, call *Alcohol & Drug Information and Referral Services*, 1-800-663-1441. For other provinces, check your telephone Yellow Pages under "Addictions."

- Another resource in Ontario is *The Addiction Research Foundation,* with a large in-patient and out-patient hospital at 33 Russell Street, Toronto, Ontario M5S 2S1 (416) 595-6100. Their programmes include a smoking cessation clinic and mental health unit, plus a clinic for anxiety and mood disorders. The ARF also provides information through their twenty-seven branches across the province; check your telephone directory under "Addiction Research Foundation," or call toll-free from anywhere in Ontario: 1-800-INFO-ARF (1-800-463-6273).

- *Alcoholics Anonymous* is a world-wide organization that has helped men and women of all ages to begin a new life of self-esteem and sobriety while protecting their privacy. Meetings of AA (and countless other unaffiliated groups which use the twelve-steps as a programme of recovery) are held regularly everywhere. To contact AA, look in the telephone directory or call Directory Assistance ("411") in your area.

- *Check the telephone Yellow Pages* in your area for additional resources; look under "Addiction." The Toronto volume contains nearly half a page of listings for public and private clinics and services.

- There are also specific resources available for those who grew up in homes where substance abuse was a problem, often *self-help and support groups* with or without professional facilitators. Call AA for information on "Adult Children of Alcoholics."

- Many *books, magazines, newsletters and resources* are available for those interested in issues of addiction, dependence and abuse. Look in your local library or bookstore, or ask your family doctor.

Freedom from drug and alcohol dependency can lead to a new appreciation of the small pleasures of life: curling up with a good book on a stormy winter evening; walking in the woods on a crisp fall morning; lying on the beach on a bright summer day; enjoying the first tulips and daffodils on a warm spring afternoon. The changing seasons in all their beauty are an ideal metaphor for the journey of life, and their beauty is best enjoyed without the interference of chemicals, poisons that play havoc with peace, health and self-esteem. There is hope and help available for everyone everywhere. It is never too late to change.

28. Neglect

Depression touches even the little things in life. One survivor recalls his darkest days with gentle humour: "Eventually I started neglecting my appearance. My weight shot up because I couldn't be bothered exercising or eating properly. It was all too much trouble to get my hair cut or press my clothes. To be honest, I was a mess. I remember going to a party on one of my worst days. Oh, the shock on my friends' faces when I walked through the door! In a few weeks, I had changed from 'well-groomed and handsome' into 'overweight slob.' I had stopped looking in the mirror."

Depression can jeopardize careers, marriages, and families. Some of its symptoms are major and life-threatening: suicidal thoughts, self-hatred, and drug or alcohol abuse. But the small details of life also reveal the presence of this disease. Neglecting our appearance can be an important clue that something is very much amiss inside. Listen to the language we use when we ignore these simple habits of daily living: "I just can't be bothered these days."; "Who cares what I look like?"; "Nothing really matters anyway." This is the language of despair on an intimate, personal scale. We justify our neglect with high-sounding excuses: "There are more important things in life."; "I've got better things to do."; "I've been too busy lately." These grand explanations hide a simple, sad truth: in the pit of self-hatred we don't really care about ourselves in any way.

It is certainly true that there are more important things in life than the latest fashions. Choosing simple clothes and functional hairstyles is not a sign of mental illness, nor is deciding to live without cosmetics, hair colouring and nail polish. However, depression often causes us to neglect the basics of hygiene and grooming: taking a bath or shower, cutting our hair, brushing our teeth, washing our clothes. This neglect spills over into other areas of life: cleaning our homes, caring for our possessions, paying our bills. Soon there are more and more reasons to feel guilty or ashamed. After all, look at the mess we are making of absolutely everything. We look terrible; our homes look terrible. Who wouldn't *feel* terrible? Neglect that touches more and more aspects of life is part of the spectrum of depression.

On the other hand, the physical pleasure of caring for the body sends powerful signals to the mind. Enjoying a long, soothing bath or shower; spending an extra moment to sew a button or fold our clothes; massaging cream into chapped, dry hands; taking time for a hair cut: these are very simple acts in themselves, but added together they help to say, "I care about myself, all of myself, my body as well as my soul and my mind." Every time we do anything to make ourselves feel better, we take a small but important step on the road to recovery. First of all we reinforce the process of self-discovery that may have begun in a therapist's office: exploring the heart and the mind invites us to look again at the needs of the body. Secondly, simple acts of grooming and hygiene are concrete steps that we take alone, a reminder of our personal responsibility in the long process of healing. Finally, the virtue of humility grows stronger every time we recognize our normal, human needs, including the need to be comfortable. By acknowledging our right to feel better physically — choosing to wear clean clothes, deciding to wash our hair — we are reinforcing our right to feel better in every aspect of life.

Much of life is habit. Depression is the time to encourage a whole range of healthy habits that highlight the basic goodness of life. Some depressed patients are asked to keep track of the pleasant and unpleasant events that are part of each day. Then they examine why there are more negative than positive events: "What happens in my life that keeps me from enjoying myself?" It may never be possible to understand all the roots of depression. Do I feel depressed because life has so many unpleasant moments? Or does life have so many unpleasant moments because I am depressed? Whichever came first, we are encouraged to incorporate regular pleasant activities into our daily routine, including simple and satisfying grooming habits.

Those who are in the depths of severe depression may not be able to use such simple self-help strategies; instead they may require hospitalization and careful medical supervision. But many of us who suffer mild and moderate varieties of this common mental illness can take an active role in teaching ourselves to enjoy life again. We will look at other practical suggestions in the next chapter on inertia.

Many of the Psalms celebrate our faith and hope in God's loving kindness. Psalm 131 is one such song of trust. It ends with simple words of confidence which all of us can say in God's presence; with one powerful but simple image it honours the most basic human needs:

> I have calmed and quieted my soul,
>   like a child in its mother's arms.
> My soul within me is like a child
>   that has finished nursing at its mother's breast.

> (Adapted from the *Jerusalem Bible* translation.)

Cherished, caressed, washed and dressed, fed and put to sleep: trust in God has made the writer of the Psalm as serenely happy as a child. My trust in God can also help me to find the strength to love myself, right down to the smallest detail, believing that it is important to cherish and caress myself, with a clean body in clean clothes, to love myself, a child loved and wanted by God.

29. Inertia

"A body in motion tends to stay in motion;
a body at rest tends to stay at rest."

Many of us who suffer from depression know all about Newton's first law of motion quoted above. We sit listlessly in front of a window without enjoying or even noticing the passing parade; we lie in bed, daydreaming about nothing and nobody. We let the work pile up on our desks and in our homes, phone calls waiting to be returned, laundry waiting to be folded. The inertia of depression is like a bad dream: we're stranded in a vast ocean of green jello, desperately trying to escape, but our movements are slow, laboured, endlessly tedious, full of futility, until finally and gratefully we wake up.

Waking up from the inertia of depression is considerably more difficult than waking up from a bad dream: sooner or later, all bad dreams come to an end, but we may require professional assistance to shake off the nightmare reality of depression. Thankfully, in most cases depression can be treated successfully, allowing us to escape from listlessness, disinterest and boredom. As we saw in the previous chapter on Neglect, certain self-help strategies are important tools in the process of recovery. This is equally true when dealing with inertia. Newton may not have recognized depression, but "a body in motion tends to stay in motion; a body at rest tends to stay at rest."

Fitness itself, the body in motion, is one of the greatest weapons at our disposal in the war against depression; we will look at this topic in greater detail in Part IV of this book. In fact, many activities can reinforce what we learn in therapy and sustain us during the bleakest moments of sadness and despair. Group experiences like singing in a choir or working on a community project remind us of our connections to the wide world outside us. Simple pleasures like walking to the store to buy an ice cream cone reassure us that happiness still exists. Any positive, healthy activity that gives us a new perspective on our problems — a meal with friends, a visit with a grandchild — lifts the cloud of depression for even a few short hours and strengthens our confidence that recovery is possible. The list of helpful activities that are valuable in combatting depression is almost endless: read a book, go for a walk, write a letter, enjoy a bath, listen to music. These are good techniques for anyone coping with a stressful life! Unfortunately, the very nature of depression makes it supremely difficult to *begin* any activity, no matter how positive or stimulating; we have been "at rest" for so long that it takes some special force to put us "in motion."

How do we start? Experts in time management have useful suggestions on how to tackle complex or daunting projects, such as re-organizing a messy desk. One experienced executive recommends beginning with the first piece of paper at the top of the pile, whatever it happens to be. This technique recognizes an important principle: *the hardest part of any project is getting started.* Once we have actually begun, momentum soon develops and ultimately sustains us. During depression, however, it takes a courageous leap of faith to find the necessary inspiration to take the first step. And why? Because we ourselves have decided to act! We might say, "I want to take a bath because I enjoy feeling clean and relaxed. I have chosen to go for a walk because I know that the fresh air will make me feel better. I plan to cook a meal because I realize that good food helps me to cope." These are positive statements of personal choice. Now compare these less effective, negative reminders based on duty and obligation: "I'm supposed to take a bath because my family expects me to"; "I have to go for a walk because the experts say that everyone should exercise"; "I must eat sensibly because the Canada Food Guide says so."[8]

Every time we reinforce the simple idea that "I want and need" something and therefore "I can act" to satisfy myself, the mind is sending profoundly important signals to the brain, signals that say, "There is hope"; "I am important"; "Things will improve"; "I can do something to help myself." Furthermore, every time we succeed in doing something, no matter how small and insignificant, we make it easier for the next time. By accomplishing something — anything! — we provide positive reinforcement to shore up sagging self-esteem. During depression, we

---

[8]   For further information on procrastination and how to cope with inertia, see David D. Burns, M.D., *The Feeling Good Handbook* (New York: Plume Book/The Penguin Group, 1990), Chapters 9 and 10.

often "write our triumphs in the sand and carve our failures in granite."[9] If depression has kept us stuck in the rut of inertia, activities of any kind give us a chance to triumph, to accomplish, to succeed, to enjoy, and, ultimately, to recover.

Studies on depression have found that certain self-help activities are especially valuable: doing something positive and enjoyable for oneself; doing something positive and helpful for others; exercising, singing, dancing, and even praying.[10] Those who are sunk in the severest depressions may not be able to follow such advice, but many of us who have recovered from a mild or moderate bout of depression can. When we recognize certain early warning signs — the growing unwillingness to be with others; the return of sleep disturbances; a change in appetite — we can take action. By starting to move before inertia slows us down completely, we can prevent a major relapse, making the lows of depression less severe and less painful. By setting body and mind in motion with healthy habits, we prevent ourselves from falling too deeply into the trap of inertia.

30. Doubt

Everyone knows one or two confident souls who seem to think that they have solved all of life's problems. These are the people who appear to be absolutely sure about everything. I am not one of this number, nor am I alone with my hesitations and misgivings; most of us feel confused and apprehensive at times. We look for answers, while wondering if we really understand the question. We know what it means to doubt.

Doubt in fact is not always a bad thing. Since the human journey has its share of crossroads and dead ends, hidden entrances and dangerous curves, we are well advised to proceed with some caution. Marching blindly through life can be foolish indeed! However, slowing down, taking time to think while weighing our options, gives doubt the opportunity to

---

[9] Adapted from a suggestion in Bonnie McCullough, *Totally Organized the Bonnie McCullough Way* (New York: St. Martin's Press, 1986), 31.

[10] Vicky Rippere and Ruth Williams, eds., *Wounded Healers: Mental Health Workers' Experiences of Depression* (Chichester: John Wiley & Sons Ltd., 1985), 179. Other forms of self-help activities mentioned include "playing the recorder." As a life-long musician I can personally testify to the healing power of making music.

sneak inside. In one of life's ironies, doubt can exist only where there is also choice, and human existence is based on the ability, indeed the necessity, to choose.

The most destructive doubts involve our feelings about our own inner resources, our essential worthiness, our ultimate value in the universal order of things. Too often when we are depressed, we identify ourselves with our mistakes; from all the self-images available to us, we *choose* the ones that say "incompetent and undeserving." We perceive ourselves as worthless failures, especially in comparison to others whose triumphs we envy. Trapped in the habits of over-generalization and "twisted thinking," we assume that everyone else understands the meaning of life. We alone still struggle to make sense of this challenging existence. Everyone else, of course, seems happy, confident and useful all the time, while we are plagued with feelings of sadness, insecurity and uselessness. Anyone who is sensitive to life's complexities sometimes feels doubt and a variety of other so-called negative emotions; however, not everyone turns doubt into a weapon directed primarily at the self.

What can we do to reverse self-doubt: our negative thoughts and feelings about ourselves? Many of us who suffer from depression can be helped by new therapies that work specifically to change the way we think. These *cognitive therapies* teach us to refute our overly critical judgments, to change the tape of negative thoughts that plays over and over again in our heads. Many of our thinking patterns and habitual responses to stress, failure and disappointment can be traced to childhood, when we unwittingly began to imitate our parents' attitudes to the negative events of life. We originally learned to be optimists or pessimists at home; in cognitive therapy we discover healthier, more hopeful ways to think about ourselves and our problems. Cognitive therapy also teaches us to unravel the habits of self-doubt or "twisted thinking" that can undermine self-confidence and lead to feelings of hopelessness, anxiety and frustration. Such therapy often includes specific exercises to be done between sessions, like mental health homework; the workbooks which teach these techniques are readily available for those who want to work independently. For further information, see the Appendix.

Once we have recognized that inside our depression we are a mass of insecurities and misgivings, we can take the first steps to change the direction of our doubts, perhaps by using the methods of cognitive therapy. Doubt can be a very useful tool, the starting point for humility and hope, an opportunity to acknowledge our fallible, apprehensive and uncertain humanity and approach the only completely certain element in this ever-changing world: our loving Creator in our midst. Part of this cognitive therapy, that is, our way of re-conceptualizing the way we talk and think about reality, may include shifting our spiritual perspective. We can start by recognizing that God loves each one of us personally. Then, instead of seeing our relationship to our Creator in terms of a human quest for God, let us remember the biblical picture of God in search of us. Jesus told a parable of a shepherd who loses one of his many sheep; the good shepherd will leave behind the ninety-nine sheep who are safe in the flock to search for the one that is lost in the wilderness. This comforting image, as well as the words of Psalm 23, "The Lord is my shepherd," invites us to focus, not on ourselves, lost and still searching, but on God, who has already found us.

Doubt at its best teaches us to appreciate the mysteries of this world, including God's hidden or disguised presence. Doubt can teach us compassion, as we recognize that others too can be confused and apprehensive. Doubt can inspire us to look for new challenges, more fruitful relationships, better ways to use our time and talents; doubt can keep us from getting stuck in a rut of complacent self-congratulation. Doubt can help us reflect on the unique role played by each individual in the eternal drama of life. Destructive doubt can lead to self-hatred, but a positive approach to doubt can be the beginning of humility and hope. In this way, doubt can lead to prayer, an ongoing dialogue rooted in faith, a conversation between One who is the Answer, all-powerful yet infinitely loving, and one who continues to question, fragile, limited, yet truly loved.

31. Fatigue

Years ago I wrote the following description of fatigue in a letter to an old friend: "During the worst days, my life had this pattern: wake up exhausted; drag myself out of bed; eventually go to the office late; perk up after lunch to do a few hours' productive work; slip back into exhaustion by late afternoon; eat supper; watch TV; sleep for a couple of hours, then toss and turn until 4 am; sleep for a few more hours; then wake up exhausted to start all over again."[11]

Others who suffer from depression tell a similar story about fatigue, one of the most common symptoms of this truly debilitating disease. They describe the immense effort needed to accomplish even the simplest household tasks, the terrible struggle required to finish a project at work: "I get out of bed morning after morning, never rested, never refreshed"; "I'm always tired"; "I have barely enough energy to take a bath or cook the dinner." Those who have never suffered in this way may not realize what it means to cope with the weight of fatigue, a ball and chain dragged by a weary body that seems to be moving from habit and discipline alone. Such exhaustion is frightening. After all, other people do all sorts of things, day after day: work regular hours, care for the house, take night courses, garden, exercise, and on and on. What can possibly be happening?

Comparing our exhaustion to everyone else's energy only makes us feel worse. Maybe there is something really wrong! An overactive imagination spins through a cycle of horrendous possibilities: "Perhaps I'm so tired because I have a brain tumour, a rare blood disease, an incurable cancer." And so it goes, week after week, until finally we seek help or the depression begins to lift on its own. While it lasts, however, this dreadful fatigue belongs to the deepest level of some imaginary hell, a place where life and energy are drained from a tortured body, a body that is not allowed to sink into the blessed release of death.

Those suffering from depression are not alone in their experience of fatigue, a symptom that belongs to many other illnesses and chronic conditions. Women after childbirth; victims of stroke or heart attack; those who suffer from rheumatoid arthritis, AIDS, or diabetes; most post-operative patients: all these and others know what it means to be profoundly, even nauseatingly tired. Perhaps this is why it is so easy to ignore fatigue as a symptom of depression. Furthermore, the demands of career and family responsibilities cause many people to complain about lack of sleep, tiredness and overwork. Why is the fatigue of

---

[11] Letter to Father James Wells, OFM, October 7, 1993.

depression any different from the exhaustion experienced by many commuters, busy parents, shift workers or harried executives?

On closer inspection, it appears that the fatigue of depression is not helped by many of the normal, useful techniques that sustain others who have demanding, tiring lives. A chance to sleep late on the weekend, three or four days' holiday at the cottage, a nap in the afternoon, a few early nights: these restoring activities often provide little or no relief to those who are depressed. Because sleep disturbances are often present, afternoon naps often make the situation worse. Likewise, many depressed people stay in bed for the regulation eight hours per night, but the quality of their sleep is so poor that they don't feel rested or refreshed. Those who wake up regularly in the middle of the night know the empty darkness of the hours after midnight when life's prospects look bleak indeed. Furthermore, some people sleep far more than usual during depression and still feel tired. Sleep is evidently not the answer to the problem of fatigue and depression, for recovery from depression requires more than just adequate rest.

Four hundred years ago, the poet George Herbert reflected on the gifts showered on all humanity during the creation.[12] Strength, beauty, wisdom, honour, pleasure — God poured out these jewels and more. Only Rest remained in the bottom of the glass which contained every blessing. And God refused to pour out the final gift, recognizing that Rest, alone of all these treasures, might turn our gaze away from our Creator, letting us worship the pleasures of this creation instead. Weariness seems to belong to so many stages of the journey of life. Can there be some purpose for exhaustion? Perhaps the poet was right all those years ago, and fatigue is the ultimate opportunity for us to learn true humility, patience and trust. Today, self-worth is equated with energy; too often we are judged by our ability to get things done. Forced to cope with fatigue, some of us finally cast off the pride that blocks us from recognizing our human needs, our human wants, our human limitations. The world's riches, the glass of blessings poured out upon this earth, are wonders to behold, yet they are not always enough to fill us with faith, hope or love. Fatigue,

---

[12]   "The Pulley" by metaphysical poet and Anglican priest George Herbert (1593-1633).

for all its horrors, may lead us at last to seek, to pray, to cry, and to surrender.

32. Agitation

Along with fatigue and sleep disturbances, there are other physical symptoms associated with depression. Sometimes we feel edgy, restless, and distracted; more graphically we might say, "I can't sit still," or, "I'm ready to jump out of my skin." Nail-biting, hair pulling, constant movement, wandering concentration, or darting eyes: this agitation reinforces the "nervous wreck" stereotype of mental illness, the troubled mind in conflict with the ordered rhythm of the universe.

Our physical agitation may be caused by depression; at the same time, there are spiritual dimensions to our restlessness. Everyone craves peace and serenity, the elusive goals of harmony, happiness and contentment. Sometimes we dream that winning a lottery will solve all our problems, as though we could somehow create a soothing oasis for ourselves if only we had enough money in the bank. We search for entertaining diversions, turning to actors, athletes or musicians to distract us from who we are and what we suffer. Unfortunately, our problems come with us wherever we go; they will still be waiting for us when we finally come home again.

Sometimes we hope to rest our restless hearts in activity: throwing ourselves into our work; looking for new mountains to climb; cramming more and more projects into an already busy schedule. Or we try desperately to believe that some revolutionary new philosophy, religion or political movement will finally bring about the peace that has been sorely lacking, individually and collectively, in this troubled world. Perhaps change is the answer: a different career, a better house, or the novelty of a transfer to another city. How many of us fondly hope that love and marriage will bring direction and completion to our previously vacant and aimless lives? Unfortunately, no matter how much we do, spend, give, take, build or buy, we cannot manufacture tranquillity. We may succeed in distracting ourselves or disguising our problems for a while, but as long as we are alive — pulsing, growing, changing, learning — our journey to eternal peace is still in progress.

At the same time, the agitation of depression is a useful warning signal that we need help; we were not created to live with chronic restlessness and overwhelming frustration. Once again, it is worth remembering that eighty percent of those suffering from this common mental illness can be helped, while researchers continue to look for new treatments for those who have not responded to current ones. No one should be resigned to depression forever. Yet many of the questions that we ask about the nature of peace, the source of contentment, the possibility of serenity and the need for satisfaction are questions that every one should ask.

All religious thought in the West has been influenced in some way by our separation from our Creator, our exile from our true home in God's kingdom. However much we may love this world and enjoy this present life, we have not yet arrived at our final destination. Once again, we are confronted by a fundamental tension in human life: this creation has been graced with many blessings, yet there is still so much that remains unfinished, incomplete, unresolved. We ask questions about the meaning of suffering, and the large and small tragedies that each of us has personally experienced; we experience "the scandal of God's absence"[13] and try to reconcile this with faith in God's eternal presence. Jesus' first words to his disciples after the resurrection were "Peace be with you!"[14] "Shalom," the Hebrew word for peace, is commonly used as a greeting throughout the Bible. We believe in God's promises to us, the covenant that exists between ourselves and our Creator, yet we know that we hold this faith in the midst of conflict, pain and trial.

Can we ever find contentment within ourselves? Perhaps not. Or perhaps not completely. An existential emptiness exists at the core of every human heart. Sometimes our consciousness of the void within us leads to irritation, agitation, restlessness; sometimes we try to fill this aching emptiness with things, accomplishments, activities, distractions. But whatever we do will never be enough; no human being, no matter how

---

[13] This idea is explored at length by John F. Haught in *What is God?* (New York: Paulist Press, 1986). In his introduction, Haught says, "If God is a reality, why is this reality so unverifiable, so elusive? Why, as Freud asked, should that which holds the most importance for believers, namely God, be so lacking in immediate obviousness to themselves as well as to non-believers?" (7).

[14] John 20:21, 26.

powerful, rich or talented, will ever be complete in this life. We cannot be everywhere and do everything. We cannot *be* God. As St. Augustine, someone who wandered long in the wilderness of interior conflict and doubt, once prayed so poignantly, "Our hearts are ever restless, until they find their rest in You."

A catalogue arrived at my house the other day, with tempting advertisements for tranquillity tapes, serenity wind chimes and relaxing bath oils. Also featured was a coffee mug printed with this quotation: "For peace of mind, resign as general manager of the universe," a witty, expression of the importance of distance, balance and perspective in life.[15] Psalm 42, written many hundreds of years ago, likewise deals with the need for tranquillity, serenity and relaxation. The very first line of this psalm focuses on the yearnings that are part of all human life: "As a deer longs for flowing streams, so my soul longs for you, O God." As the psalmist reflects on his own agitation, his lack of peace and contentment, he repeats this refrain: "Why are you cast down, O my soul, and why are you disquieted within me?" Like each of us who still waits for eternal peace and harmony, the writer knows that there can be no completion just yet. To live with the tension in his restless, agitated soul, he reminds himself to hope, as he pours out his soul in tears and prayer, thirsting for the presence of God in a world that is sometimes lonely and frightening:

"Hope in God; for I shall again praise him, my help and my God."

33. Sadness

Some years ago, two Toronto churches[16] jointly sponsored a weekend presentation on the writings of John of the Cross. This great sixteenth-century Spanish mystic, poet and saint used the phrase "the dark night of the soul" to describe his experience of God's absence; during his short life he knew desolation and ecstasy, doubt and faith, pain and joy. His

---

[15] From *Signals — A Catalog for Fans and Friends of Public Television,* WGBH Educational Foundation, Boston, Mass., Fall/Winter 1995.

[16] "Dark Night," a presentation by Father John Welsh, O.Carm., February 28 and 29, 1992, co-sponsored by Blessed Sacrament Catholic Church and St. Clement's Anglican Church.

insights and spiritual growth were formed by his appreciation of emptiness; in the dark night within himself, he touched the void that only God can fill. During the workshop, one of the participants, an Anglican priest, pointed out this common misconception concerning religion and human emotions: some people unrealistically believe that those who have faith are supposed to be happy, cheerful and content all the time. John of the Cross in his wisdom recognized the value of spiritual anguish and emptiness. We in turn can be reassured that it is a part of life to feel lost, lonely and sad.

The sadness of depression goes beyond the experience of spiritual emptiness. It is part of a medical condition that can and should be treated. Regretfully, only one out of every three people with depression will receive accurate diagnosis and treatment.[17] What a tragedy! For the sadness of depression can create bitterness and despair, poison our relationships with family and friends, drive us to desperate acts of destruction and anger. At the same time, sadness can also teach us to cherish the emptiness that only God can fill. It can be a blank wall that shuts out all light and happiness or a doorway that leads to an appreciation of the fragile beauty of this creation. Sadness can lock us away in a lonely room where we nurse our own wounds in bitterness and isolation, or it can open a window into the pain of others who also suffer. Living with sadness can be an opportunity for us to grow into caring, thoughtful individuals who have learned humility, compassion and perseverance. After recognizing our own weaknesses and insecurities, we will hesitate to look with haughty disdain on the failings of others. Living in the shadow makes us appreciate the sunshine; we are less tempted to take the warmth and energy of happiness for granted.

The sadness of depression is not caused by a failure of faith; it is not a punishment for past wrongs or a trial that must be endured without recourse to treatment or medication. Accepting depression as a gift does not mean abandoning hope. On the contrary: realistically accepting sadness also means realistically accepting the potential for recovery.

---

[17] From *Depression in Primary Care: Detection, Diagnosis and Treatment,* Agency for Health Care Policy and Research Publication No. 93-0552, United States Department of Health and Human Services, Rockville, Maryland, April 1993, 1.

Likewise, the other symptoms of depression can be faced in a positive way. The courage to endure fatigue, inertia and agitation is the same courage needed to accept treatment; the healing of a lifetime's accumulation of anger, guilt and shame can change our willingness and ability to forgive others. Depression can cause us to neglect our needs and doubt our abilities; honesty and humility lead to a sincere acknowledgement of our human yearnings, our human gifts, our human nature. Love is the only antidote to destructive self-hatred; strengthened by God's love, we can learn compassion and charity for all human creatures, including ourselves.

The Scriptures, especially the Psalms, contain many expressions of thanksgiving. Everything that lives and breathes is called to praise the Creator, using trumpets and cymbals, harps and lute, strings and pipes, a symphony of gratitude and glory. In Psalm 30, however, we see a more restrained appreciation of the blessings of creation: "Weeping may linger for the night, but joy comes in the morning." The writer remembers his tears of sadness, his dismay at God's absence, his life in the wilderness of spiritual exile: "O Lord my God, I cried to you for help and you have healed me." He does not pretend that every moment of his life has been full of joy and satisfaction. This juxtaposition of sadness and thanksgiving can reflect our similar experiences with depression: "You have turned my mourning into dancing; you have taken off my sackcloth and clothed me with joy." This is a realistic, grown-up and faith-filled understanding of the sunshine and shadow of human existence.

The sadness of serious depression may be a symptom of a medical illness, but as human beings we suffer in many ways — body, soul, mind and spirit. The sadness should be treated medically; in Part I of this book we reviewed various therapies and treatments. We do ourselves a great disservice, however, if we try to treat one aspect of our nature while ignoring the whole of our humanity. By recognizing the spiritual dimension of the symptoms of depression we give ourselves the opportunity to grow, while at the same time deriving comfort and strength from God. Treating the complete human person is the most positive way to approach any illness.

And so we return to John of the Cross, with whom we began this chapter. John may have walked in the darkness of his own suffering, when he experienced the pain of God's absence. But John also points to the "sparks of new life, the hidden turning points where the flame [of God's love] no longer only pains but begins to heal."[18] We too can use the experience of sadness — the sadness of depression, bereavement, disappointment, in fact, the sadness that is part of any life that is lived to the fullest — and transform our pain into a positive experience rooted in faith, hope and love. For God will be with us on every step of the journey, wherever that may be, in the sunshine or in the shadow.

---

[18] John Welch, O.Carm., *When Gods Die* (New York/Mahwah, N.J.: Paulist Press, 1990), 202.

Part IV

Into the Sunshine

... practical advice on fitness, relaxation and nutrition ...

Body and soul
The body in motion
Finding time for fitness
The body at rest
Relaxation
Rules of sleep hygiene
The food factor
Bread and ashes: for those who hate to eat
Coping with cravings
The meaning of pleasure
The journey of life

34. Body and Soul

Those who are new to depression are often surprised to discover that physical complaints are associated with this mental illness. We expect to find sadness and crying, symptoms that belong to the world of mood and emotion, but not sleep disturbances, stomach upsets and eating disorders. After all, depression is called a "mental" illness. Why is the body affected as well? This question reveals a fundamental problem in our attitude to health and sickness alike. We forget that we are composed of body and soul, mind and spirit; anything that affects one part of the human person can affect the whole.

There are many reasons why we ignore our interconnected needs and desires. Some of us have inherited negative attitudes towards the human body, distrusting and fearing anything that reminds us that we are not pure spirit. For a combination of cultural, historical and religious reasons, we may have established a silent hierarchy of values, allowing the body some few paltry rights which are nevertheless far inferior to the claims of the mind or the soul. Exercise, rest and nutrition are all very well, we might say, but they are less important than lofty spiritual or intellectual pursuits. Does having a rich spiritual or intellectual life also mean that we shouldn't enjoy the pleasures of the five senses: the touch of a friend's hand, the scent of a rose from the garden, the taste of freshly baked bread, the sight of tulips in the spring, the sound of bird song in the morning? Others are afraid that acknowledging the limitations of the body is an admission of weakness; they assume that strong people naturally rise above the need for food, sleep and exercise. After all, many successful types boast that their hectic schedules allow little time for recreation, making the rest of us embarrassed to need a good night's sleep and three meals a day.

Thankfully, the truth is very different: strong people can also be prayerful, sensuous, imaginative, graceful, pensive, playful, loving and intelligent; strong people are allowed to be hungry, tired, restless, thirsty, and even depressed. Happiness means many things, but it certainly includes balancing the needs of the body with the needs of the soul, mind and spirit. We are most likely to live in peace with ourselves by respecting all that we are as complex human beings.

One day, when I was in Grade VIII, Mr P. our teacher quoted a few words of Latin at the beginning of health class: *"mens sana in corpore sano,"* and explained that we should have "a healthy mind in a healthy body."[1] He didn't bother with the whole quotation, something I didn't discover until many years later: *"You should pray to have a sound mind in a sound body."* These words are appropriate here, where I have stressed the relationship between spirituality and health, mental and physical. Some of the connections between mind and body are well known. We often say that physical exercise — a brisk walk in the fresh air — is helpful after intense mental exercise like thinking, writing, or studying. Nervousness, anxiety or other moods obviously affect us physically: before giving a speech we have "butterflies" inside; pressure and deadlines can lead to tension headaches. These are simple, everyday examples of the link between mind and body. More subtle are the connections between mental illness and less obvious physical symptoms. Look at the common problem of sleep disturbances. We often ignore the

---

[1]   Juvenal (60-130 AD.), *Satires* 356.

possible association between daytime depression and sleepless nights; as we have seen in previous chapters, sometimes we try to treat our symptoms without truly understanding their roots in other illnesses.

Furthermore, if it is difficult to recognize all the points of connection between mind and body, it is even more challenging to accept the relationship between body and soul in the overall picture of health and sickness. Nowhere in Scripture are there any specific commandments that say, "Thou shalt not neglect thy exercise programme," or, "Remember to eat wisely this and every day." Unfortunately, some devout and prayerful people pride themselves on indifference to the body. In ages past it was a mark of the saintly life to eat little and sleep less; think of the holy hermits who lived in caves and slept on the ground. For those subsisting on roots and berries, the pleasures of this world were nothing more than a snare and a delusion; the best way to protect the soul from the temptations of the flesh was to hold most of this world in contempt. How many sincere, even saintly, people forgot that God looked at the work of creation and saw that it was good?[2] Likewise, illness became a welcome opportunity for noble suffering. In their perhaps short-sighted austerity, these ascetics scorned the prospect of health, happiness and contentment.

The rest of this book will demonstrate a different perspective on life: embracing, not ignoring, the connections between body and soul, celebrating, not despising, the lessons that can be learned from health, happiness and contentment. Instead of hiding behind fear of our physical nature or contempt for it, we will welcome the need for exercise, relaxation and nutrition. Most importantly, we will look at practical strategies for using the wisdom of the body to cope with the stresses and strains experienced by the mind and spirit. The challenges of life cannot be eliminated by starting a fitness programme, enjoying long baths or preparing sensible, well-balanced meals, but there are healthy ways to cope with any problem, including the problem of depression.

Long ago, the writer of Psalm 84 sang, "How beautiful is your dwelling place, O Lord of Hosts!" Using the image of the courtyard belonging to a mighty ruler, he expressed the hope that one day he too would live in

---

[2] Genesis 1:4, 18, 21, 25, 31.

God's house, body and soul together. Inspired by this psalm, let's look at different aspects of God's *dwelling place*. First, we might think of paradise, the heavenly Kingdom of perfection, grace and completion. God's *dwelling place* is also a temple, church or synagogue, a beautiful building used for community worship. We also recognize that God's image can lie within the other people whom we meet on the journey of life, because every person has been blessed with an eternally precious, eternally lovely human soul.

Psalm 84 also inspires me to remember my Grade VIII teacher and his words of wisdom when teaching health; Mr. P. would explain that each one of us was a temple of the Holy Spirit, and for that reason, our bodies were precious gifts that we should treasure and even reverence. Mr. P.'s words remind me that I too am God's *dwelling place*, a vessel of divine grace, a place of beauty and peace, regardless of the shape of my body, my physical condition, my human strengths and weaknesses. I believe that others are worthy of my love and respect since they carry the imprint of their Maker's hand. I deserve the same love and respect because God can also live within me, within my whole self, including this humble and sometimes misunderstood body. There is no special compartment in the human person that is marked, "Soul: the place which God has touched." If God is like sunshine, as the writer of Psalm 84 imagined, the rays of God's love and energy shine down everywhere: on body, heart, imagination, intelligence. Learning to love the whole human person with all its needs can change our approach to the journey of life, leading us out of the shadow of depression and into the sunshine of God's presence here and now in this world.

35. The Body in Motion

Progress can be wonderful. Who would want to return to earlier days when slavery was accepted as a fact of life, few people could read and write, infant deaths were commonplace, and all surgical procedures dangerous undertakings? The world has cause to rejoice in today's advances in human rights, education, medicine, and technology; however, there is one area where Western society has not shown any improvement. If anything, we have deteriorated. Compared to our ancestors, we no longer appreciate the human need for movement — the body in motion.

Research has shown that exercise is necessary for good health; experts can demonstrate how to exercise safely and effectively. Yet, in spite of all our knowledge about fitness and the human body, we as a society are unwilling to translate theory into practice. Recently released figures gathered by Statistics Canada tell a sorry tale: less than seventeen percent of Canadian adults exercise regularly.[3] I often wonder if this decline in physical activity is related in some way to the increase in depression and stress-related illnesses in our world. Progress has led us to ignore Nature's greatest built-in tranquillizer: regular exercise.

Exercise helps the human mind and body in many ways: improving circulation, lowering blood pressure, controlling cholesterol levels, relieving stress, changing sleep patterns, clearing the mind, and relaxing the spirit. The process of "getting in shape" strengthens heart, lungs, muscles and practically every other organ of the human body. Furthermore, many doctors and therapists prescribe exercise, especially aerobic exercise, as a partial antidote for depression, because it gives patients an increased sense of self-discipline, control and mastery.[4] Knowing all these positive benefits to fitness, what should we do? We have available an enormous variety of physical activities to be enjoyed, alone or in groups, in public and in private, in health clubs and resorts, gyms and recreational centres, with Nautilus machines, jogging tracks, swimming pools and basketball courts just waiting to be used. Television programmes and video cassettes bring fitness classes, yoga instruction, stretch and strength workouts, weight training, and more into homes everywhere. The world of fitness offers something to suit every taste, budget, age and physical condition. Yet we sit, doing little or nothing. We have become one gigantic body at rest, plagued with the diseases of

---

[3] From an article on the end of the fitness boom in the *Toronto Star*, Sunday, September 24, 1995.

[4] From *What you should know about women and depression,* a brochure prepared by the Office of Public Affairs, American Psychological Association.

inactivity in the midst of material plenty. Why have we become so physically unfit?[5]

The previous chapter explored some of the ways we distrust the needs of the body because of a distortion in our spiritual beliefs. We also undervalue the importance of exercise because of our misunderstanding of progress. Intellectual activity has become more important to our society than physical labour. Exercise strikes many of us as all too similar to manual work, something we went to school to avoid! Furthermore, unless we are a member of a tiny elite of professional athletes, anything we do as amateurs will be woefully inferior to the performances that make headlines at the Olympics or in the Super Bowl. Our puny endeavours on the tennis court or at the golf course hardly compare to the thrill of watching real professionals in action. We have become passive *consumers* of entertainment and not active *participants* in sports, games and recreational activities. And then there is that mixed blessing, the car. Today, most of us don't walk: we drive. The car, the great liberator that was supposed to open up unlimited vistas of opportunity, has trapped us all in a prison of physical neglect.

Thus we sit and stagnate, ignoring some of the greatest gifts bestowed on us: movement, play, grace, satisfaction, and beauty. How much we lose when we decide that real life for adults means chaining ourselves to our work, sitting at our desks for hours on end, and then using precious leisure time to sit even more! It doesn't matter if we use that "precious leisure time" to sit in front of mindless television programmes or at uplifting symphony concerts. As a society, we have forgotten our origins as creatures made to rejoice in movement. As a result, many of us no longer know what it means to feel fully human — alive, healthy, energetic. What a shame!

Furthermore, exercise has a host of positive side-effects that are important for those suffering from depression:

---

[5] A note for those who are curious about my own fitness interests: my favourite activities are slow and steady aerobic exercises like walking, running, swimming and hiking. Since 1980 I have exercised three to five times a week, an invaluable help during times of great stress. While writing this book, an intense and sedentary project, I made a special point of exercising as much as possible.

- *Vigorous exercise creates positive chemical changes in the brain:* the nervous system releases anti-depressant neuro-transmitters such as endorphins. Exercise helps to dissipate the pressure-cooker feelings that are associated with stress, anger and unresolved tensions.

- *Regular exercise helps to control food cravings,* a problem sometimes associated with depression and anxiety.

- *Exercise influences sleep patterns.* Fit people spend more time in the deepest, most satisfying stages of sleep, so they wake up feeling rested and restored.

- *Moderate exercise significantly lessens the symptoms of PMS* (premenstrual syndrome), especially the feelings of sadness and anxiety.

- *Regular exercise changes mental attitudes,* helps to overcome inertia and fatigue, and introduces a host of positive accomplishments to those who have been feeling worthless and hopeless. Setting fitness goals and then reaching them — running a mile, swimming 10 lengths — is a positive and powerful experience.

Improved self-esteem, renewed energy, greater resistance to minor ailments: the list of the benefits of exercise goes on and on. As one book on depression states, "Without a doubt, there are very few medical and psychological treatments with as many advantages (and as few undesirable side-effects) which are as inexpensive as regular physical exercise."[6]

Perhaps you are a member of the majority here in Canada, the eighty-three percent of all adults who do not get enough exercise. If you are also trying to cope with depression, anxiety or stress, now is the time to take positive steps towards feeling better. A sign in one doctor's office sums up the rewards awaiting those who start to move, slowly and

---

[6]   Richard F. Berg, C.S.C., and Christine McCartney, *Depression and the Integrated Life* (New York: Alba House, 1981), 119.

tentatively at first, but eventually with confidence and strength: "A fifteen-minute walk after dinner can change your life." [7]

36. Finding Time for Fitness

Unfortunately, there are many well-placed roadblocks on the journey to fitness. The body at rest resists the voice of conscience suggesting that it's time to start moving! We stall by recalling horror stories of joggers struck down by heart attacks on the side of the road, swimmers who developed shoulder problems, or hikers who were attacked by bears. Any excuse will do. Sometimes we resent the unrealistic claims of those who exaggerate the benefits of fitness. Exercise may be part of the arsenal of weapons that are effective in the ongoing war against depression, yet it doesn't cure everyone and everything. I have known triathletes, long distance cyclists and competitive swimmers who were clinically depressed, marathon runners who abused alcohol. Remember the example in Chapter 4 of the rabbi who excelled at squash? In spite of his excellent physical condition, Daniel also battled serious suicidal fantasies and required medication to climb out of the pit of despair.

Furthermore, many people discover that finding time for fitness is considerably more difficult than the exercise itself. Experts recommend three to five sessions of vigorous activity per week, each session lasting thirty minutes or more. If fitness is new to your life, you may need to re-arrange your schedule to reach that goal. So, for those who juggle many roles and responsibilities, a few tips on finding time:[8]

- Fitness is not achieved merely by working out in the gym or taking aerobics classes. Don't focus exclusively on "exercise." Instead, *enjoy an active lifestyle*. Some ideas: wherever possible, take the stairs, not the elevator; walk to the store; play with the kids. Work around the house or garden: rake leaves, shovel snow, mow the lawn, or wash the floor. Try to accumulate thirty minutes of "active living" on most days, as the foundation of the exercise pyramid.

---

[7] With thanks to chiropractor Elaine Dembe, whose bulletin board always contains sound advice on the wisdom residing in the human body.

[8] Adapted from suggestions by Dr. Elaine Dembe, *Passionate Longevity: The 10 Secrets To Growing Younger* (Toronto: Macmillan Canada 1995), 95-98.

Then add aerobic conditioning, strength training and flexibility exercises. Love your body by using it!

- *Make an appointment with yourself for fitness.* Silly as it might seem, writing down an appointment in your daily planner will strengthen your commitment to fitness.

- *Exercise with a friend.* The buddy system is recommended for beginners who need all the encouragement they can find.

- *Exercise in the morning* when you are less likely to be distracted by sudden emergencies; your time is usually your own at 6:30 AM! However, if no time is the right time, schedule a little of everything in the week: one morning workout, one noon-time walk, one afternoon workout, and one or two weekend activities.

- *Set realistic goals* appropriate to your age, current fitness level and other responsibilities. A new mother won't have the time or the energy to train for a marathon; a student usually can't afford to join an expensive health club. Don't make discouraging comparisons with others. Similarly, when returning to an exercise programme after a lengthy lay-off, don't expect to regain your previous level of fitness overnight. As is so often advised, accept your limitations.

- *Be creative in reinforcing your commitment to fitness.* Write down your goals, start a fitness diary (mine is decorated with colourful stickers), and chart your progress. Promise yourself a reward for following your programme: some new exercise clothes, or a special weekend holiday.

- *Never let yesterday's failures discourage you today.* So you acted like a vegetable and ignored all your good resolutions. Never mind — God invented morning to give you a second chance every day!

- *Be flexible.* When the weather is too miserable for cycling, try an exercise video on your VCR; if you have some unexpected free time, go for a walk. Never restrict yourself to one and only one sport. Find activities that you can enjoy in winter and summer.

- *Join a health club.* Making new friends who are interested in fitness can be a great motivator. Clubs offer many different types of activities to combat boredom, as well as fitness tests, personalized programmes and professional instruction on exercise techniques and equipment.

- It may be difficult, but force yourself *to put your needs first.* The concept of making time for fitness may be foreign to you, especially if you are accustomed to seeing other people's needs at the top of your list. *A serious commitment to your own well-being is the most important factor in finding time for fitness!*

A few words in praise of walking

Walking is often called the best exercise. It costs absolutely nothing, requires no special clothes or equipment, and can be enjoyed anywhere in the world, twelve months of the year, twenty-four hours a day. Unlike more vigorous activities, walking rarely leads to fitness injuries. Walking can be a solitary, personal experience or a pleasure to be shared in a group. Walkers explore city streets, country lanes, nature trails, indoor tracks, shopping malls; they enjoy misty mornings, bright sunny days, dramatic sunsets, peaceful evenings. For those who want more challenge, walking can lead to running, hiking, orienteering; it can also remain a gentle stroll after dinner. Walking can be as natural as breathing, yet many of us have forgotten the pleasure that comes from this simple and satisfying activity. The easiest way to find time for fitness is to rediscover the joys of walking.

Finding time for fitness can be one more powerful, positive step on the road to recovery from depression. As the experts say, "Exercise is the most reliable mood-elevator known."[9] A healthy lifestyle includes time for movement, time for pleasure, time for fitness.

---

9   Covert Bailey and Lea Bishop, *The Fit or Fat Woman* (Boston: Houghton Mifflin Company, 1989), 103. Bailey's *Fit or Fat* series of books, videos and television programmes offer effective, well-researched information on the body in motion.

37. The Body at Rest

"And on the seventh day God rested."

Genesis 2:2

The Scriptures include one surprising detail in their account of the origin of our world. The poetic mind that wrote the powerful story of the beginning of all things depicted God wanting to rest after the strenuous business of creation! In this way God made rest a holy activity. In the wisdom of our ancestors, one day a week, Saturday or Sunday, was set aside to remember God's own desire to take a break. In many cultures, unfortunately, the Lord's Day observances became unnecessarily strict, as if rest should be equated with boredom and punishment. In my father's time a boy was not allowed to throw a ball in a park on Sunday. Now, most of these old-fashioned ideas about honouring the Sabbath, good and bad alike, have been tossed out the window. Just as we have lost our appreciation of the human need for movement, progress and secularization have likewise weakened our commitment to regular, healthy rest.

In today's economic climate, with the ongoing threat of cutbacks, recession and job insecurity, many employees are made to feel that rest, leisure, recreation and relaxation are expensive luxuries that they cannot afford to enjoy. Work comes first! God could afford to rest, but productive men and women have to do without such pampering. Many otherwise reasonable people despise our human need to rest. Robert describes his father's attitude towards leisure: "My poor father died of a heart attack in his early sixties. He was a driven man, working seven days a week for most of his life. Home was the place where he rested up so that he could go back to work in the morning." Listen to these comments about another successful executive made by his former assistant: "Charles never liked weekends; there was nothing to do at home and he couldn't wait to get back to the office on Monday morning. He hated retirement and did not live to see his seventieth birthday."[10]

---

[10] Names and some details have been changed.

Lest these two masculine examples lead anyone to assume that women have healthier attitudes towards work and rest, let me describe one high-powered woman doctor who has trouble tearing herself away from her office for a few weeks' vacation every year. She ruefully admits that she does not practice what she preaches to her patients. Another woman ignored her doctor's advice and checked herself out of the hospital a few hours after major surgery because she "didn't have time to be sick." What do all these attitudes towards rest say? Think of the proverbs quoted by mothers and fathers alike, words of wisdom which extol the virtue of work while undermining the importance of rest: "Idle hands are the devil's workshop"; "Don't just sit there: do something!"; "A little hard work never killed anyone." Can there ever be a happy medium, a way to find a balance between laziness and overwork? How should we honour our need to rest?

It is impossible to define how much rest is "enough." One of the most important ways that humans rest is through sleep, a process that is crucially necessary for both physical and mental health, for growth, bodily recovery, and overall well-being. Some of us need more sleep than others; the average in our society may be seven to seven-and-a-half hours per night (less than in the past, by the way)[11] but there are wide variations between individuals. Some of us love to nap, while others claim that resting during the day is a physical impossibility. Once again, notice the importance of recognizing our individual needs when thinking about rest. Since sleep disturbances are often part of the experience of depression, the next two chapters will deal with sleep and relaxation in greater detail.

Accepting the importance of rest in the balance of a healthy life is the first step for many of us learning to cope with the stresses and strains of modern life. Personal ambition sometimes prevents us from taking time

---

[11] Peter Hauri, Ph.D., and Shirley Linde, Ph.D., *No More Sleepless Nights* (New York: John Wiley & Sons, Inc., 1990), 28. The authors state: "About 150 years ago, before Thomas Edison developed the electric light, our entire society slept about an hour longer, a little more than eight hours. Some people say it hasn't hurt us any to stay up longer . . . that all we do is sleep a little more soundly and deeply. Other people say that the frenetic pace of our modern living has to do with Edison's giving us light and leading us to stay up longer than we really should" (9).

away from the consuming quest for success. A popular magazine recently contained a profile of an energetic television personality who needed only four hours of sleep per night. Several teachers discussed the article with me; most of them envied this ability to do twenty hours of work each and every day. The story of the celebrity who didn't need to sleep affected me differently: I recoiled in horror from this glorification of productivity run amuck. How much must we do to be successful? How many things do we need to buy or build in one lifetime? When our lives are over, can we take even one of our triumphs or creations with us? Are we trying to cheat death by amassing so much in this life that the sheer weight of our possessions and accomplishments will chain us to this earth forever? How much is enough?

Finding a balance in life means taking time for people, for nature, for the ordinary events of every day, while believing that all our needs (including the need to rest) are important. It often seems that the contemporary veneration of productive activity is motivated by the fear of silence and peace, fuelled by our reluctance to spend time alone with our innermost thoughts and feelings. Finding a balance in life means defending the need to rest, regardless of our society's misguided emphasis on winning at any cost and working as much as possible. Constructive, healthy idleness, far from being the devil's workshop, is a necessary part of the human journey. "On the seventh day God rested." How much rest do you need?

38. Relaxation

Hand-in-hand with learning to rest is learning to relax. It is difficult, if not downright impossible, to sleep soundly in an anxious, troubled and preoccupied state of mind. The following suggestions focus on some of the ways to restore the restful balance between body, soul, mind and spirit.

One powerful way to relax is through *bodywork* — one of the various forms of therapeutic massage.[12] The typical massage therapy studio is a

---

[12] Reputable massage therapy clinics employ registered therapists who have received extensive training in anatomy and other medical subjects at recognized colleges. Ask your family doctor, chiropractor, or other health care provider for a referral to a reputable clinic.

quiet, tranquil space. Soft, gentle music — harps and flutes mixed with the whispers of the wind — may play in the background. The physical contact that is part of the treatment contributes to the process of relaxation, for massage therapy honours the age-old need for touch shared by humans and animals alike. Are your shoulders and neck stiff from sitting too long at a desk, legs and feet weary from standing too long at a counter? The aches and pains of living are soothed by the therapist's trained, healing hands. Likewise, the stresses and strains of the mind won't disappear on a massage table, but they will take on a different perspective as the body begins to relax. The relaxation provided by massage is especially valuable when body and mind have been in pain through depression or anxiety. In the weeks after my father passed away in 1979, I found that everything ached after a day of sitting at a desk; a friend suggested massage, and since then I have tried to make time regularly for this ancient healing technique.[13] But there are other roads to relaxation as well.

We have already looked at some of the positive benefits of fitness programmes in the treatment of depression, especially vigorous aerobic activities such as walking, running and swimming. *Gentle stretching exercises*, yoga, tai chi and the meditative martial arts also contribute to the body's need to relax and unwind. By turning the mind away from the often troubling thoughts and worries of every day, *yoga and other meditative exercises* provide much needed moments of stillness to comfort both body and soul.

Exercises which are designed to help the body relax are often practised in silence or accompanied by gentle, soothing music, and today, more than ever, we need all the *silence and music* we can find. Hell has been called the Kingdom of Noise. Imagine the torture that could be caused by eternally ringing telephones, the incessant drone of traffic, and the non-stop hum of machinery. But never mind Hell: silence has become an increasingly rare commodity right here on earth! Open plan office designs make it very difficult to concentrate at work; even at home it is hard to retreat in peace, because of blaring radios and televisions, the

---

[13] With thanks to the gifted therapists who have brought relaxation and healing to me through massage, especially Judy Pustil, Alix McLaughlin, Barbie Lane, Aileen McKenzie, Witold Dobrzanski, Anthony Madott and Marjorie Lewis.

interruptions of families and neighbours, and the reluctance to remain quietly alone with our innermost thoughts and feelings. Silence and music, in and of themselves, are excellent tools to help us relax, especially for those whose lives are at times overwhelmed by distraction and noise.

Then there is water. Swimming pools, saunas, steam rooms and whirlpools may be luxuries found only in health clubs, resorts and the occasional well-equipped mansion, but everyone has the opportunity for a little home-made *water therapy*. Never underestimate the value of long relaxing baths and bracing cool showers. Try running through the lawn sprinkler during the next summer heat wave! Human beings love water, the tranquil element that washes us clean, physically and symbolically as well. Some busy executives use water therapy to make an effective transition between *work* and *home*. By having a bath or a shower as soon as they return from the office, they are "washing away" the preoccupations of the day while preparing for the rest and relaxation that belong to life at home.

Likewise, we can draw on *the power of nature* to help us relax. Walking on a treadmill while looking at a blank wall has virtually the same exercise benefit as walking outdoors through a park or along a beach. Nevertheless, putting our feet in touch with the earth, feeling the wind and the sun on our faces, has a value far beyond fitness. It is no accident that corporate designers turn to the outdoors when they want to create visual statements about the "good life" of peace and prosperity; think of all those terrific photographs of mountain ranges, unspoiled beaches and rugged hiking trails used to sell everything from cars to soap. Although most of us have chosen a sedentary life in an urban environment, marketing experts have discovered that everyone loves images of vigorous outdoor activities pursued in settings of great natural beauty. So, if you are looking for another helpful tool to cope with stress and depression, why not return to what all human beings seem to know solely by instinct? Anyone who has ever told a rambunctious youngster to "Go outside and play" has recognized the power of outdoor activities to channel young energies in a positive and healthy way. This remains good advice for everyone, young and old alike.

Unfortunately, the human need to unwind is often translated into "watching television" or "going shopping," activities that numb but never really relax either a tired body or a troubled mind. Millions of us consider the passive consumption of entertainment to be the appropriate way to spend most of our precious leisure hours. Television is especially disappointing as a relaxation tool: regardless of the content of the programmes we watch, a few hours in front of the TV screen creates a dull, vacant restlessness that is not true relaxation. There are thousands of psychotherapists, relaxation experts and stress management consultants in this world. Not one of these trained and experienced professionals would advise their patients to "go home and watch television" or "binge on some cookies" or "have too much to drink" or "wander through the mall spending money" when coping with anxiety or depression. Yet this is what many of us do when we feel low. The line of least resistance takes us right to the television set, the cookie jar, our credit cards or the liquor cabinet. Like a drug that promises to deliver us from pain and frustration, only to create its own problems of dependence, these less-healthy responses to stress and strain are seductively attractive when we need to unwind. Unfortunately, they often become part of the problem of depression, rarely part of the solution.

If you are looking for more positive ways to relax, try anything that includes *play, fitness, music and the great outdoors*. These positive and healthy activities send powerful messages to the brain which say, "Hello, World! I'm alive and well and in control. Happiness is important to me, and I want to learn how to enjoy life again." Recovery from mental illness often includes serious commitments of time, energy and money for therapy and medical treatment. Making time for relaxation is also necessary when fighting the chronic self-hatred and neglect that are part of depression.

39. Rules of Sleep Hygiene

Part A) For Those Who Can't Sleep

"I lie awake; I am like a lonely bird on the housetop."

Psalm 102:7

Insomnia can take many forms: some sufferers can't fall asleep, some can't stay asleep, some wake up too early. Experts feel that more than half of all insomnias are caused by psychological problems such as depression, anxiety, marital or job stress.[14] Don't try to cure the symptoms of your sleep disturbances without tackling their origins as well. The following suggestions will help you to cope while your depression or anxiety is being treated:

- *Avoid sleeping pills except as a short-term measure.* Because there are many causes of sleep disturbances, there are no easy solutions. With time, sleeping pills usually become part of the problem because they interfere with the body's natural rhythms.

- *Restrict your time in bed.* Going to bed earlier and earlier in order to catch up on lost sleep is ultimately self-defeating. Fewer hours of deep, refreshing sleep are better than more hours of restless, light sleep. *Go to bed and get up at the same time every day.*

- *Be careful with naps* which often interfere with good night-time sleep. Some retired people fall into the habit of dozing throughout the day and then are unable to sleep soundly at night. If you do nap, establish a pattern by resting at the same time every day.

- *Avoid caffeine!* Limit the use of coffee and tea (switch to decaffeinated varieties), cola beverages, chocolate, and some pain killers (read the labels.) Some people are especially sensitive to this potent drug; coffee even in the morning or afternoon may affect their night-time sleep. See Chapter 27 for suggestions of adult non-alcoholic beverages that are caffeine-free. As the experts

---

[14]   Hauri and Linde, *No More Sleepless Nights*, 28.

say, "Caffeine in the evening disturbs sleep even in those who feel it does not."[15]

- *Use alcohol wisely.* Some insomniacs believe that a few drinks help them to fall asleep, but alcohol usually interferes with sustained, deep sleep. Likewise, *do not smoke,* as nicotine disturbs the natural sleep/wake cycle. *Do not take non-prescription sleeping pills* or street drugs ("downers") which are dangerous and potentially habit-forming.

- *Make your bedroom a relaxing haven associated with sleep. Never work in bed!* If you have negative feelings about a room associated with sleeplessness, try some simple, restful re-decoration: a new coat of paint (think pastels), new bed linens or draperies. Re-arrange the furniture. If your partner snores, try ear plugs, separate beds or even separate rooms. Be willing to experiment.

- *Exercise helps promote deep, restorative sleep*, especially exercise in the late afternoon. Or try a walk after dinner. However, very intense, vigorous activity (running, aerobics) just before bedtime often causes the opposite effect, leaving many people too wide awake to sleep.

- *Don't go to bed right after a heavy meal.* And conversely, *don't go to bed hungry.* Make a light snack part of your bed-time rituals. Some people swear by cookies and milk, or herbal tea (especially camomile). Also, try toast and jam, cereal, porridge, or even light broth. Some sufferers are helped by calcium and magnesium supplements.

- Don't go right from *work* to *bed. Schedule a cool-down time* beforehand. For example, if your official bed time is ten o'clock, stop work at eight and spend the next two hours unwinding: reading, relaxing, doing light stretching exercises, enjoying a long leisurely bath (aim for half an hour soaking in the tub), listening to music.

---

[15] From the pamphlet *Insomnia: The Facts,* from Sleep/Wake Disorders Canada, Toronto, Ontario, no date.

- If you wake up in the middle of the night and can't fall back asleep, *get up and go into another room.* Read, write letters, embroider, fold laundry — any quiet, repetitive task — until you feel sleepy again. Have a cup of herbal tea or warm milk, then try again. Repeat this procedure if necessary later in the night. *Don't lie awake in bed watching the clock and fretting about lost sleep.*

- If all else fails, *get professional help.* Read a book on sleep; talk to your family doctor; try massage, yoga, meditation; consult a relaxation expert. Call your local hospital for a referral to a sleep disorders clinic. More and more specialists help those plagued by poor sleep.

- As your depression lifts, your sleep will probably improve, so *work on regaining mental health through professional treatment and self-help activities.*

- Brochures, tapes and printed material, as well as information on local chapters and sleep laboratories, are available from Sleep/Wake Disorders Canada, 3089 Bathurst St., Suite 304, Toronto, Ontario M6A 2A4, 416-787-5374, or 1-800-387-9253; fax: 416-787-4431.

Part B) For Those Who Sleep Too Much

"Can't stand the sight of myself,
Lying in bed all day with the curtains drawn."

"House of Dreams," Blue Rodeo[16]

Then there are those of us who take refuge under the covers when we are depressed, sleeping much of the day and all of the night. The bedroom becomes a safe haven where we can hide from our negative thoughts and feelings. One woman describes her sleeping this way: "I used to have many doubts, fears and recriminations, like a tape playing a theme of self-hatred over and over again in my head. Sleep was the only way I could cut off the tape." When the inner and outer world is a hostile

---

[16] Blue Rodeo, "House of Dreams," from *Diamond Mine*, Warner Electra Atlantic CD-56268, 1988, 1989.

117

place, there may be nowhere left to retreat but in sleep. A few suggestions for those who sleep too much:

- If you are tired all the time, sleeping more than usual without feeling rested, do not assume that this sleep pattern is related to depression. *Check with your family doctor first:* other medical problems may be causing your fatigue.

- Likewise, drowsiness is a common side effect of many over-the-counter and prescription medications, including some antihistamines, some cough and cold remedies, some tranquillizers, many antidepressants. *Ask your doctor or pharmacist to review your medications.*

- After ruling out medical or drug-related causes for sleeping too much, help yourself by resolving to *make concrete plans for everyday.* Ask yourself, "How do I want to spend my time? Why do I want to get out of bed?" A job or other commitment often provides excellent motivation to start moving in the morning. Otherwise, try to make specific arrangements to go somewhere or do something. *Structure your time* to help you get started.

- *Exercise!* Once again, exercise works wonders in improving moods, strengthening your commitment to recovery, and reinforcing the help you may also be receiving through therapy or medication.

- *Beware of alcohol.* As we saw in Chapter 27, alcohol is not a stimulant as is commonly supposed but a powerful depressant that will eventually make life look very bleak indeed. Using a few drinks as a "pick-me-up" is a dangerous habit to begin.

- Likewise *avoid all non-prescription stimulants* or street drugs ("uppers"). These can be habit-forming and at the very least interfere with the natural sleep/wake cycle of the body.

- Although you may be sleeping far longer than usual, the quality of your sleep is often poor. For this reason, *practise the rules of sleep hygiene* for those who can't sleep. Difficult as it may be, *avoid caffeine and tobacco* which interfere with the natural sleep/wake cycle of the body.

- *Do everything possible to reinforce the contrast between "awake" and "asleep."* When you get up, make yourself feel as alert as possible: open the curtains, take a brisk shower, get dressed, eat breakfast, go into the fresh air as soon as possible. *Don't hang around the house all day in nightgown or pyjamas!* Likewise, try not to lie down or nap until bed time. This is equally valuable advice for those who can't sleep.

- *Recognize that there are certain times of the day when you feel better* and use that to your advantage.[17] If you are a night owl, give yourself a head start on the next morning by choosing your clothes, setting the breakfast table and preparing your lunch in the evening, when you are still fresh and energetic. If you are an early bird, schedule important meetings or start your fitness programme in the morning.

- And finally, anything that helps to alleviate depression will indirectly affect your sleeping habits. *Review the suggestions for self-help activities* found in Chapter 28, "Neglect"; Chapter 29, "Inertia"; and elsewhere in this book.

40. The Food Factor

What shall we eat today? How about a nice bowl of steaming hot porridge for breakfast? Would you like a hamburger and french fries for lunch, or would you rather have a grilled chicken sandwich? Barbecued steak or poached salmon for dinner, strawberries or lemon parfait for dessert? Will you have room for hot chocolate and home-made shortbread before bedtime? What shall we eat tomorrow?

The human body, like the car that runs on gasoline, needs food in order to "go." Phyllis George, native leader and manager of programmes for Anishnawbe Health Toronto, has observed that some of us take better care of our cars than we do our bodies.[18] We have looked at ways to care

---

17   "How to Make Life Easier," from the pamphlet *Now We Can Successfully Treat the Illness Called Depression*, distributed by the National Foundation for Depressive Illness, Inc., P.O. Box 2257, New York, N.Y. 10116, no date.

18   Speaking at the Annual Person's Day Breakfast, October 26, 1995.

for ourselves through fitness, rest and relaxation. What is the fuel we should put in our bodies? Twenty-one meals a week, a few snacks, fifty or so beverages. The preparation and consumption of food is the largest, most time-consuming domestic task, according to those who study the way we work in our homes: hours and hours spent shopping, cooking, serving, cleaning-up, and thinking about food.[19] Food is a form of entertainment, a status symbol, an expression of love, a weapon of control, an emotional statement about family and friendship, and a symbol of cultural identity. However important it is to eat a well-balanced, high-fibre, low-fat diet, food is so much more than mere fuel for the body.

Look again at the list of foods mentioned in the first paragraph. Everyone of us will have some feelings towards each item, positive and negative alike. You may have happy memories about Mom cooking porridge on cold winter mornings, as my mother often did; you may detest the idea of barbecued steak, dreaming instead of the lightly poached salmon fillet. Strawberries? No longer a simple pleasure restricted to June and July, these are now available year round and considered a sophisticated treat in winter. Hot chocolate, on the other hand, is often associated with warm feelings from childhood. There is so much more here than mere nutrition.

Meanwhile, it's almost time for another meal. Are you ready to eat? If you are struggling with depression, you may also be experiencing changes in your appetite. Some people lose all interest in food and have to force themselves to eat; others are ravenously hungry all the time, beset by food cravings. We will look at both these extremes in the following chapters. But if you were to create for yourself the ideal diet, something to hold up as a lifetime goal, what would you choose? How should you weigh the often conflicting advice from nutrition experts, mothers, fitness enthusiasts, doctors and gourmets, all of whom have something interesting and worthwhile to say about food? There seem to be more questions than answers.

Drawing on my experience in the food business, my research on nutrition, my love of cooking, and my struggles with depression, I try to follow this common-sense plan based on Canada's Food Guide: Enjoy a wide

---

[19] Bonnie McCullough, *Totally Organized*, 173: "The cycle of food in and out of a house, and the preparation and cleanup are the biggest process in a home."

variety of lightly processed, low-fat, low-salt foods. Emphasize fresh fruits and vegetables, whole grain breads, cereals, pasta, rice; include reasonable portions of meat, chicken, eggs, dairy products and fish. Take it easy with desserts. Drink lots of water, avoid caffeine, enjoy one glass of wine with a meal. Maintain a reasonable weight: too thin is as harmful as too fat. Ignore fads; there are no magic cures or miracle diets. Take a multi-vitamin tablet daily to guarantee adequate vitamin and mineral intake. Food is a friend, not an enemy; enjoy everything in moderation!

I can't always stick to this sensible plan, especially when life feels bleak and I am nearly overwhelmed by cravings for sweets. One wise nutritionist also reminds us that there are twenty-one meals in a week; choosing the "hamburger and french fries" instead of the "grilled chicken sandwich" for one of those meals is not a crime or a moral failing.[20] No one should feel chained to a rigid, austerely correct diet that denies the human need for foods that have special meaning in our family or society.

Our food choices both reflect and influence our moods. For example, when feeling tired, stressed or edgy, I often crave a treat like chocolate or cookies, symbols of indulgence and affection in our society. Unfortunately, looking for comfort in sweets, with their high-fat and high sugar content, usually creates more problems than solutions. The initial rush of insulin from the sugar soon wears off and in its place I am left feeling lower than before. I know that a high-fat diet may lead to a multitude of serious health problems; the human cardio-vascular system cannot operate at its best when the body is drowning in butter, lard and cholesterol. Recognizing these detrimental effects, I then regret having indulged myself in this way. On the other hand, what happens when I choose a healthy snack such as an apple or some crackers? The complex, low-fat carbohydrates contained in fruit and breads provide sustained energy for a longer period of time than the empty calories found in chocolate or cookies. I realize that I feel better after eating my healthy snack; this sends the positive signal to the mind that I am also caring for the body. My choices about food — apples versus chocolate — can change the way I feel, both mentally and physically.

---

[20]   With thanks to the "queen of common sense cuisine" Maye Musk, past president of the Consulting Dietitians of Canada, for this idea.

The words of Psalm 23 find their way into a host of experiences of life. I often quote this line when asked to say grace at a family dinner: "You spread before me a feast." How true! Whether we are eating alone or in a group, at home or in a public place, the abundance of wonderful, healthy foods available to us is like a feast spread before our eyes. We are invited to a banquet. God help us to choose wisely, enjoying with gratitude the bounty of this earth, appreciating our ability to taste and see the goodness given to us by our Creator.

41. Bread and Ashes: For Those Who Hate to Eat

Psalm 102 contains a poignant description of losing one's appetite, a common problem with depression: "I eat ashes like bread, and mingle tears with my drink . . . I wither away like grass." Some true stories of others who hate to eat:

- Nina[21] has been a widow for many years. Her grown-up children tease her that she hasn't cooked a real meal for herself since their father died. They are exaggerating, but in fact Nina hates to eat alone. She associates cooking, shopping and planning a meal with the happy family dinners of the past, and since those days are gone forever, Nina doesn't cook anymore.

- Elderly Mrs. Forsythe lives in a lovely thatched cottage in southeastern England. Unfortunately, she becomes a "tea and toast" lady who cannot be bothered to eat real meals. Twenty years of neglecting her diet eventually leads to osteoporosis and malnutrition.

- Leslie's job disappears during a wave of cutbacks in the construction industry. Because of stress, Leslie's appetite disappears as well, resulting in an unhealthy and unplanned weight loss.

Many of us have no desire for food when we are depressed: struggling with nausea and stomach upsets, we barely manage to eat a little soup, cereal or bread at mealtimes. Often we begin to lose weight which in turn makes us feel even more "run down" and "washed up." Soon we

---

[21]   All names and some details have been changed.

find ourselves especially vulnerable to minor ailments, coughs and colds which last for weeks, viruses and infections of every kind. What should you do if food begins to taste like bread mixed with ashes? If you are suffering from anxiety, bereavement or depression, good intentions alone are not enough to ensure an adequate diet. Some coping skills, however, may help until you feel more like eating:

- *Try to make meal times special.* Warned by the example of her grandmother's malnutrition, Mrs. Forsythe's granddaughter says, "I used to hate cooking; slaving away in the kitchen seemed like a waste of time. I thought I had better things to do. My grandmother's sad experiences caused me to change my attitude towards food. I learned to cook well and experiment with new dishes, resolving to eat one well-balanced meal every day."

- If eating alone is a problem, *share meals with a friend.* Find other single people and get together regularly.

- *Take advantage of the prepared meals available* in supermarkets and delicatessens. Home cooking might be your first choice, but anything is better than "no cooking."

- *Be creative* when trying to rekindle your interest in eating. Have a dinner party; make single-serving portions and freeze them; explore your local restaurants; ask a family member to take over some of the meal preparation; keep a food diary; reward yourself for sensible eating.

- *Eat frequent small meals* to combat nausea and stomach upsets. Between meals, sip on warm herbal tea, especially soothing Camomile or Peppermint. Also helpful for nausea is genuine tonic water (look for "quinine" in the list of ingredients). Or try plain hot water with a dash of Angostura bitters, a surprisingly delicious drink.

- In extreme cases, *use liquid food supplements* such as "Ensure" or "Boost" or "Essentials" to guarantee that you are receiving enough nutrients in your diet. These products are available in pharmacies.

- *Recognize that your lack of appetite is part of a bigger problem*; treatment for depression or anxiety will ultimately help your eating problems too.

- *Exercise!* If you have read as far as Chapter 41 in this book, you have seen this word before. Gentle exercise in the fresh air may help you to regain your appetite because exercise encourages a healthy perspective on the whole human body.

- *Use alcohol wisely.* Although cocktails before dinner might seem like a good way to stimulate your appetite, you may find yourself far more susceptible to alcohol because of your lower body weight or your relatively empty stomach. Try a little herbal tea or tomato juice with spices instead.

- *Maintain a healthy attitude towards normal body weight.* Our society's current obsession with thin, childlike women can have dangerous ramifications, as the pressure of extreme low-fat dieting and over-exercising may lead to depression in some women.

- *For those specifically concerned with anorexia* (an intense, unrealistic fear of being fat which leads to extreme weight loss from dieting) or *bulimia* (binge eating followed by purging through self-induced vomiting or the use of laxatives), *contact your family doctor* or:

  The National Eating Disorders Information Centre
  The Toronto Hospital
  200 Elizabeth Street, College Wing 1-211
  Toronto, Ontario M5G 2C4 (416) 340-4156

Anorexia and bulimia are serious medical conditions which can lead to long-term health problems, and even death. Recent research has shown that some eating disorders can be alleviated by the use of anti-depressant medications.

- *As the above suggestions indicate, there is hope and help available for everyone!*

42. Coping with Cravings

Like a lion on the prowl across the savannah of Africa, a stealthy figure appears on the staircase in the middle of the night. Wrapped in a warm but faded bathrobe, the midnight prowler doesn't bother to turn on a light, but quietly creeps along the familiar corridors in the friendly darkness, careful not to disturb the other sleeping inhabitants of the house. The destination of this shadowy figure? The kitchen cupboard where chocolate bars are stored.

Such is the world of those whose depression is marked by cravings for sweets, chocolates and treats of all kinds. "Treats" are defined as food items that are emotional in their appeal but not necessarily nutritious. I grew up in a house where we ate the finest fresh fruits and vegetables twelve months of the year, one of the benefits of a family in the food business. Therefore, luscious peaches or out-of-season asparagus are not "treats" for me. When I want to eat for comfort and consolation, I do not crave wholesome fruit salad or crisp garden greens; I want something sweet, especially something baked out of chocolate. And when I am tired, anxious or hurt in any way, I do not cope very well with these cravings.

Someone else yearns for crisp, salty treats like potato chips; yet another craves smooth, creamy custard. A third has no interest whatsoever in these snacks, but dreams instead of plain home cooking, wolfing down platters of bacon and eggs, fried potatoes and toast during those midnight raids on the pantry. Others nibble absent-mindedly on candies throughout the day. The link between all these eating patterns is that they are motivated by something other than true hunger. These are cravings for comfort, reassurance, escape — feelings often associated with depression and anxiety.

I confess that I have not won all my battles in the war against unhealthy overeating. If you too feel like a ravening lion day and night, you may want to try one of the following techniques for coping with cravings:

- Some people who crave certain specific items (chocolate, salty snacks) swear by the *total abstinence* principle. Don't buy it and you can't eat it; if someone brings it into the house, give it away, throw it in the garbage, hide it in the freezer, but put it out of sight. "It" can be chocolate bars or cookies, potato chips or peanuts. "It" is something you are unable to resist, and, left to your own devices, you will eat enough to leave yourself feeling bloated and sick.

- On the other hand, if diets of any kind make you feel desperate and deprived, you might try *selective rationing*. In this method, you choose to eat a small amount of whatever "it" is regularly. Dessert after dinner is more sensible than three chocolate bars in the middle of the night.

- There is also the *reward and conquer* technique, whereby a treat must be earned by walking to and from the store to purchase it, assuming a fifteen-minute walk in each direction.

- Or you might try *distance and distraction*. Remove yourself from temptation (distance) by doing something else (distraction) until the craving passes. Take a bath, wash your hair, or go for a walk.

- Others swear that *safety in numbers* works best; call a buddy who will help you resist the temptation to binge. Overeaters Anonymous uses this principle with serious eating disorders.

- Remember the Alcoholics Anonymous slogan: *H.A.L.T.* Do something positive (like preparing a healthy snack) before you are too **h**ungry, **a**ngry, **l**onely or **t**ired.

- If you are hungry all the time, *make sure you are eating a nutritionally adequate diet.* You may be short-changing yourself unknowingly. Do your meals include enough protein (meat, chicken, fish, eggs, dairy products, nuts, legumes)? Some people, especially teen-age girls, become vegetarians simply by cutting out animal products without substituting adequate protein from other sources.

- Others are hungry because they are chronically tired. *Consult your family doctor or professional nutritionist* if you are eating to cope with fatigue. You may have vitamin or mineral deficiencies.

- *Exercise!* Fitness helps the mind and body in many ways, but, surprising as it may seem, exercise helps us to develop and maintain healthy attitudes towards balanced, sensible eating. When fit people exercise, their appetite is temporarily dulled; when unfit people exercise, they often find themselves ravenously hungry. A long-term strategy for coping with cravings is to make a commitment to regular, sustained exercise.

None of these suggestions will entirely eliminate the desperate feeling of unappeasable hunger that no food can fully satisfy. Rather, these coping skills help to control the shame and guilt which follow unhealthy overeating. It is helpful to remember that certain foods have enormous psychological resonance. A character in one comic strip says, "I worked hard today. I deserve a snack. I earned a reward." She then devours a bag of treats.[22] A humorous button with the drawing of a bewildered hippopotamus carries the slogan, "If wearer is found depressed, administer chocolate immediately."[23] There is only so much we can do to change our feelings and memories about the foods we eat. If Mom always made chocolate cream pie for special occasions and it was your all-time favourite food as a child, you may have great difficulty in passing up a slice, no matter how much you believe in the value of low-fat diets today.

Furthermore, our love of sweet or salty high-fat foods is part of the legacy of evolution; coping with these cravings involves fighting an enemy that has been wired into the human brain for thousands of years. Recognize that certain eating habits are very hard to change, and minimize the damage to your self-esteem by learning to appreciate everything you eat. Then stop feeling guilty! To break the vicious circle of overeating and self-hatred ("I ate too much and now I feel like a pig so I will eat a little more to comfort myself"), start by allowing yourself to enjoy whatever you have chosen — even that chocolate bar in the middle of the night.

---

[22]   "Cathy," in the Toronto *Globe and Mail*, Saturday, November 11, 1995.

[23]   Boynton cartoon.

43. The Meaning of Pleasure

One autumn I spent a week at a retreat house in Niagara Falls; once or twice a day I would take a break from my reading or meditating to go for a walk, exercise being an important part of my life even on retreat. One rainy morning I noticed the carpet of fallen leaves on the trail. Since this was late November, the spectacular reds had already faded. There was still a wealth of colour around, every imaginable shade of brown (chestnut, fawn, tan, ginger) and grey (slate, charcoal, smoke, steel) and yellow (gold, copper, buttercup, caramel). Droplets of water on the branches of the trees sparkled like tiny white diamonds. The sky was a mass of purple clouds highlighted by a few streaks of pearl and silver on the horizon in the east. This scene of unexpected beauty on a rainy November morning filled me with pleasure, a pleasure that I have never forgotten.

So often when we are depressed, we question the purpose and meaning of suffering. Bowed down by the weight of our burdens, real or imaginary, we ask, "Why me? Why now?" In Chapter 14 we looked at some of the answers. Have we ever stopped to look at the other side of the equation? What is the meaning of pleasure? I was struck by my enjoyment of colour while walking in the woods; I have paid close attention ever since, not merely to the rainbow that graces our world, but to our human appreciation of colour in general. We love colour! Our ability to see different shades and hues may have been useful to us in the process of evolution ("Beware of red berries; they might be poisonous"). Today, however, we are drawn to colour for reasons of pure pleasure, choosing magazines because of their bright covers, loving flowers for their subtle or dramatic hues, adorning our bodies with clothing, cosmetics, jewellery, and ornaments, of every shade under the sun. The absence of colour troubles us; perhaps this is why we feel sad when blue skies have been a monotonous grey for too long. For me, this universal, deeply entrenched enjoyment of colour, something which has very little useful function for human beings, is related to our need for pleasure. And pleasure is one subtle demonstration of God's presence here in this world.

Just as we have tried to explain the existence of pain and suffering by calling on our religious beliefs, so let us do the same thing to explain the existence of pleasure. God is sometimes described as a supreme Being who is perfect Beauty, Goodness, Truth, Justice and Love; our relationship to these qualities is not a philosophically interesting abstraction but a reality. Pleasure is not an accident, any more than pain and suffering are; pleasure has a purpose in this life, just as pain and suffering do. Pleasure appears to be our response to events and experiences that remind us a little of God.

Depression, as we have seen throughout this book, is an illness that numbs our ability to feel pleasure; we have a right to do everything possible to re-awaken our sense of pleasure. God has made a good world which we can rediscover in wonder, joy and tranquillity; every positive experience is a gift that teaches us something about the Creator who made us. Recovery from depression means regaining the ability to taste a delicious meal, to enjoy sex, to rejoice in our energy and enthusiasm for living, to express our love and affection for other people. Dr. Nathan Kline, a respected psychiatrist, has written:

> The one universal symptom of every depression is the loss of pleasure and joy in those things and activities which under normal circumstances make life worth living. Oddly, the feeling of depression need not always be present, but in every depressed patient it is the lack of enjoyment that is the touchstone of recognizing the condition.[24]

Too often religious people feel that noble, pious and saintly men and women are supposed to be sombre and austere; I have heard devout Catholics assert that Jesus never laughed! Think of the words of our prayers and hymns: the world is a vale of tears, we are sinful and sorrowful: and yes, sometimes life is a hard and bitter struggle. But the other side of life is also there, the times when children play happily together in the sand at the beach, friends raise a glass of champagne at a celebration dinner, or lovers walk hand-in-hand in the park.

If enjoyment is no longer part of your life, if Dr. Kline's words about depression describe you perfectly, I urge you once again to reach out for help. The vast majority of those who suffer from depression can rediscover the existence of pleasure in this life, pleasure that is not an

---

[24] Nathan S. Kline, *From Sad to Glad* (New York: Ballantine Books, 1975), 9.

illusion, a trap or a temptation from the devil, but a very real gift from a Creator who is the source of all good things on this earth.

44. The Journey of Life

Often we say that life is like a journey. While such an image might conjure up romantic dreams of exotic foreign travel, the concept of "journey" also has its limitations. Consider the problems of modern travel in crowded and noisy airplanes, buses and automobiles, rushing from point A to point B and worrying about tight schedules, lost luggage and traffic jams. I am not very attracted to the vision of life as a "journey" if it includes such expensive and uncomfortable headaches!

More fruitful is the ancient notion that the journey of life is like a pilgrimage, an open-minded, open-ended ramble through the countryside, complete with adventures, delays and detours. A pilgrim may have a definite destination in mind, but, on pilgrimage, getting there really is half the fun. Furthermore, a pilgrimage is not a solitary exile to be endured in stony silence; rather, pilgrims sing and tell stories to entertain one another on the long and dusty roads to Canterbury and Compostella, Rome and Jerusalem. In the same way, the experience of depression is one of the detours some of us experience on the journey of life. And to our surprise, we often encounter fellow pilgrims with similar problems. Some of their stories, their triumphs and failures alike, grace the pages of this book. The wisdom that others share with us in therapy and support groups can inspire us along the road to recovery. Our fellow pilgrims teach us that we are not alone, no matter how lonely we feel ourselves to be.

Life is also a quest, a challenging journey during which the hero may be tested through rigorous trials before reaching some long-awaited goal. Depression is just such a test on the journey of life. Like knights of old who were challenged by dragons, some of us are asked to battle a silent, potentially destructive enemy that has the power to make human life feel bleak and forlorn indeed. And like the armour that a knight put on before setting forth into battle, certain gifts give us strength during our trials and tribulations: the support of friends, the grace of perseverance, and the power of prayer. Throughout this book we have taken a positive attitude towards depression by focusing on ways to fight the dragon of mental illness: therapy, medication, fitness, nutrition, and relaxation techniques. Through a variety of self-help strategies along with professional counselling and care, we can cope with the challenges waiting for us on our journey, until we reach that final destination in God's kingdom.

Life is also a voyage of discovery, an opportunity to make friends with ourselves as unique individuals loved and cherished by God. Since it is important to understand as much as we can about every part of life, including the desert places where we unwittingly find ourselves, this book has realistically examined the symptoms of depression, the thoughts and feelings that can make life seem like one vast wasteland. At the same time, the most fruitful approach to depression includes respect for the whole human person — body, soul, mind and strength. We are challenged to make sense of our experiences in terms of our faith, while recognizing that God has arranged for most of us to meet Illness at some point on our voyage.

The journey of life is also like an old-fashioned holiday excursion. Imagine a summer day when the whole family sets off to enjoy a picnic at the beach. Sometimes holidays turn into disasters, as picnics and other excursions are vulnerable to bad weather and other unexpected calamities; "acts of God" we call them. In the same way, depression can disappoint and frustrate us on our journey through life. But those moments spent in the shadow can eventually reveal many profound and surprising lessons, especially the lasting value of everyday pleasures, not just the important triumphs that occur but once or twice in a lifetime. And just as the nightmare vacation is transformed by time into a good-natured adventure to be remembered and enjoyed with laughter, so our experience of depression can over time become something that we treasure because it has made us more compassionate, trusting and free.

Each of us has uniquely different experiences of the journey, the pilgrimage, the quest, the voyage of discovery, the holiday excursion. We have reassuringly similar encounters as well. Everyone knows something of the shadows of life — disappointment, sorrow, pain — yet we are also meant to live in the sunshine. Sunshine lights up the background of life whenever we know love, the love for the self, the love of one another, the love of our Creator. There is sunshine whenever we see beauty, especially the beauty of nature, the beauty of other people, the beauty of our own existence. And sunshine belongs to every experience of pleasure — the delights of the five senses, the satisfactions of the mind, and the joys of the spirit. If we learn wisdom on the way, ultimately we will be able to give thanks for both sunshine and shadow alike. Psalm 23 is my favourite among all the hymns that praise the greatness of God the Good Shepherd. Continuing on my journey, I pray that each of us will experience as much of the sunshine as possible, the graces that belong to human life at its best; in the words of the Psalm, I pray that each of us will be able to say with gratitude and trust, "My cup is brimming full."

Appendix

For Further Reading

*First-person Accounts of Depression
and Manic-Depression:*

Duke, Patty and Turran, Kenneth. *Call Me Anna.* Bantam Books, 1987.

Cronkite, Kathy. *On the Edge of Darkness: Conversations about Conquering Depression.* New York: Doubleday, 1994.
(This includes interviews with well-known writers, actors and journalists.)

Mays, John Bentley. *In the Jaws of the Black Dogs.* Toronto: Viking, 1995.

Styron, William. *Darkness Visible. A memoir of Madness.* New York: Random House, 1990.

On Cognitive Therapy:

Burns, David. *The Feeling Good Handbook.* New York: Plume Book/ The Penguin Group, 1990.

Seligman, Martin. *Learned Optimism.* New York: Simon and Schuster, 1990.

For Adult Children of Alcoholic Families:

Whitfield, Charles. *Healing the Child Within.* Deerfield Beach, FL: Health Communications, 1989.

For Sleep Disturbances:

Hauri, Peter, and Linde, Shirley. *No More Sleepless Nights.* New York: John Wiley & Sons, 1990.

For Nutritional Advice:

Lindsay, Anne. *The Lighthearted Cookbook.* Toronto: Key Porter Books, 1988.

Musk, Maye. *Feel Fantastic: Maye Musk's Good Health Clinic.* Toronto: Macmillan Canada, 1996.
(There are many books and magazines devoted to low-fat cooking.)

Medical Aspects of Depression:

Greist, John H., M.D., and Jefferson, James W., M.D. *Depression and Its Treatment*. New York: Warner Books, 1992.
(This is a guide for lay people written by two psychiatrists.)

Kline, Nathan S., M.D. *From Sad to Glad*. New York: Ballantine Books, revised edition 1991.
(This book is especially helpful for those taking medications.)

For Manic-depression:

Duke, Patty and Hochman, Gloria. *A Brilliant Madness: Living with Manic-Depressive Illness*. New York: Bantam Books, 1992.

Jamison, Kay Redfield. *Touched with Fire: Manic-Depressive Illness and the Artistic Temperament*. New York: The Free Press, 1993.

For Those Concerned about Alcohol:

Sanchez-Craig, Martha. *Saying When: How to Quit Drinking or Cut Down*. Toronto: Addiction Research Foundation, 1994.
(This self-help book is available from the ARF. To order call 1-800-661-1111)

For Seasonal Affective Disorder (SAD):

Peters, Celeste A. *Fight the Winter Blues. Don't be SAD*. Calgary: Script Publishing/Good Health Books, 1994.

For Stress:

Hanson, Peter G. *The Joy of Stress*. Denver: Hanson Stress Management Organization, revised second edition 1986. Distributed in Canada by Stoddart Publishing Co. Ltd.

Index